SCIENCE & WONDERS VOLUME II

The Light, The Heat

Amy Joy

Ocean to Mountain Publishing
PO BOX 1116
Wallace, ID 83873
www.otmpub.com

This book is based on the true life experiences of the author, who has taken care to portray the persons and events therein with honest accuracy. Certain names have been changed to protect the guilty and innocent alike.

Books published by Ocean to Mountain Publishing are available at special discounts for bulk purchases in the United States by corporations, institutions, and interested individuals.

Bible quotations are from the New King James Version unless otherwise specified.

Photographs and art are the work of the author unless otherwise specified.

ISBN: 978-1-57821-768-7

To Dr. Darrell Hobson

Thank you for laboring over us
In the instruction of Logic
And Hebrew
And the finer points of Isaiah.

I will be grateful into perpetuity.

While additional editing took place later,
this book was primarily written during the year 2013.

Table of Contents

CAST OF REAL-LIFE CHARACTERS

PROFESSORS

Dr. Paul D. Stillwell (Geologist) - mentor
Dr. Zenith (Astrophysicist) - nemesis
Dr. "Flash" Gurden (Biophysicist) - buddy
Dr. Bob Manchester (Biochemist) - advisor
Dr. Burt Derlidger (Biologist) - cell biology professor
Dr. Vallo (Organic Chemist) - occasional employer
Dr. Dan - Chair of the chemistry department

Brothers and Sisters	Notable School Mates
Lex - big brother	Matthew - Physics armor bearer
Heather - sister	Michelle - Drinks excellent coffee
Baron - brother (twin)	Whitaker - Big and bearded
Shadow - brother (twin)	Damian - Honest pal
Whitney - sister	Stickley - Or "Stick" or "Igor"
Max - brother	Maggie - Intense lab partner
Jordan - sister	Kate - Apocalyptic Horse of Death

INTRODUCTION

I've had an obnoxious compulsion to write down my life since the 8th grade. I've recorded it all in about 60 journals piled in storage totes in the barn back home. My sister Jordan used to entertain the family in my absence by pulling out random notebooks and reading them out loud. When I found out she was doing this, I did *not* pop like a baked potato somebody forgot to stab with a fork, but it did make me want to know, "Wow... thanks Jordan. Um. Was Mom listening?"

Interesting things took place when I returned to school to get my chemistry degree, and for years I wrote down the events and conversations with care. This book is the second in a series dedicated to certain college professors, particularly Dr. Stillwell the geologist. I realized it would take time to finish the story that began in Dr. Stillwell's geology lab.

I explain a variety of things in the first book that I do not rehash in this one. You are free to start here in the middle of the tale, but suspend any inclination to think I'm a complete fool. If you've read the first volume and still think I'm a complete fool, well then at least you've done due diligence.

CHAPTER 1

SUPER NOVA

On a rainy winter evening in 1992, Tony Darmanin jumped into the back of Jeremy Benson's sweet 1973 Chevy Nova hatchback with Brandon Wright and Billy Walters. Jeremy and his dad had spent a year fixing up that muscle car, and the 16-year-old boy loved it. As soon as Jeremy revved the engine and took off, Tony knew he was in trouble. They sped down North Shore Drive in Bellingham, Washington, rain pelting the windshield. White stripes flashed past the bright headlights, but darkness cloaked each new bend on the winding road. They zoomed up on a hairpin turn, and Jeremy hit the brakes.

"The car hydroplaned on the wet pavement," Tony told me. "So, we're not slowing down, and now Jeremy can't steer."

The Nova filled with teenage boys shot off a 40-foot cliff and soared through the dark night air.

"There was a tree at the bottom," Tony said. "The car started tilting in the air, and it was going to land upside down and crush us. Instead, it hit that little tree and nose-dived into the ground. That tree saved our lives."

When I later tracked down Jeremy Benson and asked him about it, he acted sheepish and embarrassed, but he said, "Indeed. God used a tree to protect us from my stupidity."[1]

Tony awoke at the bottom of the ravine, dangling in the Nova's back seat. Pain ripped through his insides. The force of the seatbelt

---

1   Jeremy confirmed Tony's entire story, and because I found him recently and asked him about the accident, Jeremy looked up Tony and discovered they only lived a few miles from each other. Jeremy emailed me and said, "I had a great talk with Tony this morning. The first time in over 20 years. Thank you for writing about this and contacting me." I thought that was just fun.

had torn his internal organs, and the broken hatchback cover had slammed into his neck. Billy's head had cracked into the windshield, and blindness temporarily overwhelmed him as his brain swelled. Miraculously, Jeremy and Brandon climbed out unharmed.

Tony woke up again outside the car in the rain. He started pulling himself through the mud and bushes on the ravine hillside, brutal inches at a time. As he reached the top, flashlights shone in his face. People in a nearby house had seen the Nova's headlights fly off the cliff and had already called 911. The ambulance arrived and rushed the boys to the hospital.

The pain from his injuries was the worst he'd ever experienced. Tony lay conscious on the gurney as a female doctor probed his stomach and rolled him down the hallway for a CAT scan. Already Tony's veins had started to collapse, and he felt pins and needles through all of his extremities. He was bleeding out on the inside.

"If you do not go into surgery in 15 minutes, you will die," the doctor told him. "Do we have your consent to take you to surgery?"

As Tony gave her permission to save his life, a sense of excitement filled him. If they did surgery and he got better, that was great. If he died, he realized that was also great. In 15 minutes he could be standing in the presence of Jesus.

Tony told me, "It makes you realize the significance of '*O death, where is thy sting? O grave, where is thy victory?*'" [2]

They couldn't get a good picture of his organs – there was too much blood loose inside him. Tony lay on the gurney in agony, forced to wait as the hospital staff discussed their next move. They decided to try one more CAT scan before surgery.

As he lay suffering and helpless, Tony had a realization that people were praying for him. He told me, "I felt their prayers. It was the first time in my life where I could actually feel the prayers of people praying for me." It was more than just a feeling. In between the two scans, Tony's organs were healed.

This time, the CAT scan came back clear and clean. There was no sign of bleeding - no evidence of injury. The puzzled doctors decided

---

2 1 Corinthians 15:55 – King James Version.

surgery was unnecessary. Tony stayed the night in the hospital for observation and then went home.

Tony told me this story in a coffee shop in Bellingham in late May of 2010. A mere week had passed since I'd left my dinosaur prints locked inside Dr. Stillwell's lab in West Virginia. Just a week. The children and I had flown out to Seattle, and I'd gone driving to see friends and family.

I knew Tony had moved back to Bellingham, so I called him up and asked him to coffee. As we sipped our drinks, I mentioned to him, "I think miracles take place all the time. Most people don't know it, but miracles are happening to people all around us."

Tony nodded his head, his curly Maltese hair pushed back by his raised eyebrows - his brown Maltese eyes wide in agreement. He finished swallowing his coffee as he nodded.

"Well, you remember when I had that car accident?" he said to me.

"No," I shook my head. I hadn't met him then.

So, he told me the story about Jeremy Benson's Chevy Nova – the one that I just told you.

After talking to Tony at the coffee shop, I looked up his mother in the white pages and I cold-called her. I believed Tony, but the more eye-witnesses to an event, the better. I had never actually met Tony's mom, but I told her who I was over the phone and she willingly gave me her side of the story.

Alice Darmanin had raced to the trauma unit at St. Luke's Hospital ahead of the ambulance. When they brought in Tony on the gurney, she thought her son was already dead.

"He wasn't moving, and he was a grey color. My heart just sank. Of course they couldn't tell us anything. We sat there praying and praying, and the kids were calling everybody they knew to pray. We still didn't know anything about Anthony. Finally they told us that there was so much blood in the pictures they had taken, they couldn't tell if it was his liver or spleen or *what* was bleeding. They said, 'If he survives the next half hour we'll take another set of pictures.' I only heard the 'if he survives' part."

The Darmanin family knew nothing more for 45 long minutes. Finally, the doctor returned to where they sat anxiously in the waiting room.

"All she says is, 'Do you want to see your son?' We walked back there and he's sitting up. The doctor said, 'I don't know what to tell you, but we don't know what happened. We don't know where the blood came from. We don't know where the blood went.' There was no blood. There were no wounds. She said, 'He has a very nasty crack on the back of his neck.'

"Actually," Alice told me, "he should have died from that. The crack was on the hangman's vertebra, and we were told only one in a thousand survives that."

I appreciated the fact that the doctor had been a woman. It was a small detail that Tony and his mother both gave me without thinking about it. I look for those small details.

Tony's life was spared. He returned home to his family, went off to college and eventually sat there having coffee with me in Bellingham in 2010.

That wasn't the end of his story, though.

Tony told me over his coffee, "But even though God did that miracle and healed my internal organs, for the past 18 years I have lived every day with pain in my neck from when the hatch slammed into me. I've gone to chiropractors, done physical therapy and deep tissue massage, and I'm still in constant pain. People tell me, 'You just don't have enough faith. If you had more faith, God would have healed your whole body.' And I think, 'No… I have faith.' Or they say, 'You have unconfessed sin, that's why you're not healed,' and I think, 'No… I have my faults, but I don't have unconfessed sin.'"

Job's friends had the same philosophy – and they were wrong too.

A year after the accident, Tony was living in a college dorm room when he ran out of all his toiletries at one time. He said, "I squeezed out the last of my toothpaste. I used the very last of my shampoo and conditioner, and even my deodorant was completely used up. All on the same day."

Tony walked down to his bank to see if he could take out five dollars. When he checked the ATM, his balance sat at just over three bucks - too little to draw out on a Saturday afternoon.

Tony said, "Well, Lord. If You don't want me to be stinky, please help me out here."

He walked back to the dorms. As he was heading to the door, his friend Margaret walked up to him with a paper bag in her arms. She said, "I don't want you to be offended, but while I was at the store shopping this morning, I really felt God wanted me to buy these things for you." Tony took the bag and looked inside. It held shampoo, conditioner, toothpaste and deodorant.

Tony said, "After all these years, it still brings tears to my eyes. Because it told me that God really cared about me, even in the little things. And it wasn't that she gave me money. Anybody can hand you money. She handed me the very things I needed."

It told Tony something else. It told him that God hadn't merely overlooked his pain, as though it was an unimportant detail. God knew his pain, and it mattered to Him.

"No, this is what I've learned," Tony told me. "I've learned that pain is not the enemy. I have learned that God has allowed me to have this pain for His reasons and for His purposes."

That was the message of Job too...

People often think that the proper response to suffering is to be tough and pony up and push through it out of sheer determination. I don't believe for a second that's God's heart. Nowhere in the Bible does God tell His servants to be tough. He constantly tells them, "Don't be afraid," and "Trust me." Even the sparrows are precious to God, and not one falls to the ground without His noticing.

> *But the very hairs of your head are all numbered. Do not fear therefore; you are of more value than many sparrows.*
>
> Luke 12:7

Miracles take place around us all the time. They do, and more miracles took place in my life after Tony and I had that talk. But when they don't, how do we handle that?

Babylonian King Nebuchadnezzar had three Hebrew men thrown into a furnace because they refused to worship his statue. Before they were cast in, they told him:

> *If that is the case, our God whom we serve is able to deliver us from the burning fiery furnace, and He will deliver us from your hand, O king. But if not, let it be known to you, O king, that we do not serve your gods, nor will we worship the gold image which you have set up.*[3]

"But if not…" God did rescue Shadrach, Meshach and Abednego from the furnace, but multitudes of others have been violently martyred. Tony and I had both experienced miracles in our lives, but we also both lived in daily suffering. We all love to be saved, to be healed, to be freed - and in Christ we *are* spiritually and eternally - but we all have to make the decision about how we're going to handle the times in our lives when it's not so easy to give God thanks.

---

3   Daniel 3:17.

CHAPTER 2

SUMMER IN THE VAN

Figure 1 - Left: "Ducilla" and I in southern Arizona. Photo by Carla Foss. Right: Sam, Savvy, and Zekie at Natural Bridges National Monument.

S
ummer 2010 deserves its own book. We had lost Dad, and I was not about to spend the summer working while abandoning my three little ones to daycare. Randy's $50,000 in life insurance allowed me to pay for his funeral, hammer away the major debts and fix our cabin. While a handyman gutted and remodeled our rotting bathroom, the kids and I flew out to Seattle and bought a 1988 conversion van with only 71,000 miles on it. Its table and bench seats converted into a bed. Its propane stove worked.

Figure 2 - The third tire on my van blew on the Mescalero Reservation in New Mexico. A lovely local woman rescued us and took us to buy a tire.

11

We traveled in that van from Seattle to West Virginia via Texas, visiting friends and family all along the way. We saw dinosaur bones and national parks. The van blew three tires on the hellishly hot roads between Arizona and New Mexico, two on my birthday. Once we reached Texas, we lived upstairs in Joe David's fossil museum for 15 days, guarded every night by the mastodon and phytosaur skeletons on the main floor. There were floods and toads and glorious adventures. We didn't pick up 200 caged tarantulas in Arizona for my lifelong friend Carla, because they weren't quite ready when we drove through. I was disappointed.

Figure 3 - Above: Mososaur bones in the original matrix. Below left: Savannah and a temporarily befriended toad. Below right: Another friend who waddled over to listen to our singing.

"If you transport tarantulas for somebody," Dr. Stillwell quipped later on, "Do they say, 'Fangs a lot!?'

Ho ho. Ha ha.

Early that summer, I sent Dr. Stillwell an email asking whether there was anything I could do to earn credit for my cross country trip. I was going to be exploring a number of national parks with amazing geology, and I figured it would be easy to do some research. Dr. S. didn't respond. I knew he checked his email every day, and I knew he'd read my note. All I wanted was a "yes" or "no," but I got nothing. I waited two weeks then emailed again. No answer at all.

That irked me.

I asked God if I should get on Dr. Stillwell's case. All I needed was a simple answer. It was frustrating for him to not say *something*. I thought I should express my irritation, but the first verse I read was 1 Timothy 5:1: *"Do not rebuke an older man, but entreat him as a father..."* [1]

"Okay," I breathed in deeply. Then I wrote another gentle email. Silence.

Months later, Dr. S. told me, "I didn't want to tell you 'No.'"

Maybe not, but that was the answer anyway, and it would have been nice for him to just say so.

It has been difficult for me at times to entreat Dr. Stillwell with the honor due a father. It is easy for me to argue with Dr. Stillwell - to gripe at him. I have to watch myself. If I've ever been rude to the good geologist, it's in direct disobedience to my Heavenly Father, who has made it clear. He's made it clear I'm to treat the man with respect.

This was an important moment, and I think about it on occasion. The irony is that God (whom I can't see) answered me. And Dr. Stillwell (whom I can see) didn't.

---

1   KJV translation

*Figure 4 - The author, enjoying the view from Grand Canyon's South Rim.
Photo by Jordan Rahert.*

Chapter 3

Dr. Zenith

"If you ever want to crush your enemies, read Newton's stuff." - Dr. Zenith

The children and I returned to West Virginia, and school began for the fall. I started the day with Physical Geology, and that pleased me. I did have a lot of reasons to respect Dr. Stillwell, and I already liked him.

I had another problem. I also needed to respect Dr. Zenith.

I had managed to avoid Dr. Zenith for most of the spring semester, which was good because the astrophysicist frowned at me whenever we passed in the halls. Every time Dr. Zenith glowered down from one of his mismatched eyes, though, I took it as a compliment. At least he didn't ignore me altogether. I took his class that fall semester knowing that I was making a dangerous move, but I would survive. Just like Gloria Gaynor and Diana Ross.

I made an effort to diffuse tensions with the astrophysicist first thing that fall 2010 semester. I entered his astronomy-rich physics lab and glanced around for the man's desk.

Ah-hah! There it sat, at the rear of the room straight back from the door. I hunted for the seat farthest away from that writing table of his in an effort to pad the space between us. There was a good spot next to Matthew Caerphilly. I settled into a seat at the front corner of the room far away from the door. Chia Pet boy grinned at me, his blonde hair poofing out from his head like straw.

"Okay, Matthew. We have to do an awesome job in this class," I said.

"Yes we do," he agreed.

I had to do well. I absolutely had to get an A in Dr. Zenith's calculus-based physics. There was no other option.

With the grandeur of Frederick Douglass, the black astrophysicist rose from his desk and approached the front of the room, and I realized in horror that I had made a terrible, foolish mistake. Dr. Zenith didn't teach from his desk! He taught from his PowerPoint station, absolutely smack beside me. I had settled into the perfect spot to receive his daily personal attention - right in the line of fire. I glanced around the room, but it was too late. The other seats were all filled.

I'd been prepared to stow away my pride at the physics lab door, and it was a good thing. About a month into the semester, my fellow student Damian described the pain of the situation in one sentence. "If I'd been sitting next to you, I'd have moved long ago."

No kidding.

When I did well, Dr. Zenith said nothing. When I made a mistake, he pointed it out. If I didn't understand something, he got irritated with me.

One day, I dropped a marble-sized steel ball. I waited for a moment to see where it would roll before reaching down to grab it. He had no patience and informed me, "You know, you should pick that up." When I didn't turn the page in my lab notebook because I was busily taking notes, Dr. Zenith flipped it over for me and said, "We've moved on." He didn't simply speak it either. He drew it out, "We've moved ooooon." In general, Dr. Zenith treated me as though I were a fourth grade child.

I didn't really mind it. I didn't mind the daily shame.

I told Matthew, "Okay, the game is to see if I can get through a Dr. Zenith class without being rebuked for something."

Two weeks into school, I almost did it. After I'd left class, I received a merry text from Matthew that said, "Amy Joy, Dr. Zenith says if you need it, he'll teach you how to push your chair in properly ;)"

Thank you, Matthew. You Dr. Zenith toady.

Damian partially blamed me. "You're always writing in your journal and writing notes to Matthew," he accused me.

Actually, I was furiously writing down the brilliance from Dr. Zenith's mouth! And I only wrote a note to Matthew... twice... commenting on something Dr. Zenith had said.

In other words, I didn't help things much.

Ironically, Dr. Zenith thought I wasn't paying attention to him because I spent so much time writing down everything he said. I struggled to capture every luminous word from his mouth, and rather than recognizing my dedication, Dr. Zenith accused me of not listening.

"Amy Joy!" he barked at me the first week of school. "This is dimensional analysis, which is why I told you to work out the UNITS!"

Oh. Yes, sir. I get it now.

Units are our best friends in math. Meters and kilograms and seconds and newtons and amperes and henries. They tell us how to set up our problems. They hold the keys to the universe.

Dr. Zenith was not like most professors. In most university classrooms, students can come in late and slip into their seats with no fuss. It's not polite to be late, but the professor will rarely say anything about it. Dr. Zenith *locked the door*. If we were late, we had to knock, and Dr. Zenith may or may not have let us in.

In most university classes, assignments are collected at the end of class. Dr. Vallo gave us until 5pm to hand in our Organic Chemistry papers (and even later if we asked nicely). Not Dr. Zenith. Lab reports for the previous week's lab were due at the beginning of class, stapled and placed in the pile alphabetically according to our last names. Dr. Zenith would then correct the stack of reports and record our grades in his grade book in precise sequence. I am not joking even a little. Alphabetical order.

Other professors might let students take a few extra minutes to finish a test after the class time has ended. At the least, they permit students to keep going until the next class of students starts wandering in. Dr. Zenith's tests ended on the hour. That was it. He offered no extra minutes.

Dr. Zenith made it clear the first day of school that we were to return our tools and balances and measurement devices to their cupboards at the end of class, and we were to always *always* push in our chairs.

It almost made it worse that I sat next to Matthew. Matthew the future engineer had a brilliant mind for math, and Dr. Zenith adored him from the beginning. Glowing Matthew provided a glorious contrast to my status as the tick-infested, hairless goat-blood-sucking chupacabra.

"Matthew!" Dr. Zenith pointed at the young Mr. Caerphilly one day. "You explain this to the class!" And Matthew did. He walked us through a kinematics problem, and Dr. Zenith jotted on the white board the solution exactly as Matthew dictated.

"Do you see how he set up his formulas?" Dr. Zenith frothed in admiration. "Do you see how he rearranged the equation so that his unknown is on one side and the rest of the problem is on the other? Do that!" Dr. Zenith made an X across his chest with his arms and told Matthew, "All the love, man."

I used the white board after class one day to draw out a solution for a friend, and all the love Dr. Zenith gave me was, "Hey Amy Joy. Don't get any ink on my PowerPoint screen."

Once he started teaching, though, something magical would happen to the astrophysicist. He morphed from the pretentious lord of the classroom into this remarkably hilarious standup comedian. A spotlight focused on the physics professor center stage. The supernova of the hour flared the room with his marvelous personality, erupting giggles across his class. Yes. Giggles.

We learned almost immediately of a prophecy concerning Dr. Zenith's death.

"I do not joke about ninjas," Dr. Zenith warned us. "There's a prophecy I'll be killed by ninjas."

"There's a prophecy you'll be killed by ninjas?" Matthew frowned.

"Yes," the professor affirmed with no humor in his voice. Dr. Zenith is all about gravity.

Straight up, Dr. Zenith put a whole lot of zest into our physics education.

"Let me explain to you the difference between instantaneous velocity and average velocity," Dr. Zenith told us early in the semester. Energetic. Full of charisma. "So, you're driving down the road at 55 mph in a 35 mph zone, and a police officer pulls you over. You could accept the ticket, or you could do what I do and say, 'Mr. Officer, look. Here's my stopwatch. I left my house at 8:05 am. See, I took a picture on my phone. I then spent three minutes at the stoplight.' Get out your little white board," Dr. Zenith urged us. "*I* do. And draw out your route. Make a diagram. 'Here's the path I took. So you see, Mr. Officer, averaging the time it took for me to get from my house to here, you should actually give me a ticket for going too *slow*.' But, the officer doesn't care about your average velocity. He only cares about your instantaneous velocity at the moment you passed him."

Dr. Zenith's animated personality filled the room, and I sat there snickering and trying to scribble it all down.

Good old Stickley came late to class one day and had to knock on the door. In a moment of grace, Dr. Zenith allowed him in. The next day, Stick behaved according to wisdom and brought Dr. Zenith a large Three Musketeers candy bar, cradling it in both hands like a box of frankincense.

"Dr. Zenith," Stick said. "I was in the book store, and I bought two Three Musketeers bars. But, I'm full now and I thought you might enjoy this one."

"I would very much. Thank you," said Dr. Zenith.

That candy bar did not serve as a fine or bribe or any other cheap, gutter purpose. Stick offered it as a gift to the beneficent emperor of the classroom, and unlike stale old Dr. Stillwells, beneficent emperors must of course accept free-will offerings from their subjects.

In October of 2012, I flew back to West Virginia to square away some things with my cabin. I had long developed a friendship with the young physics professor "Flash" Gurden and his wife Amanda. During my visit, Flash and Amanda invited me to their autumn bonfire. A variety of other professors made appearances, and Dr. Zenith and his wife arrived at the party at about 7 o'clock bearing a glass jug filled with a curious blue liquid.

"Dr. Zenith!" I declared when he entered the Gurden home. "The man of the hour! Sir, would you like me to have the trumpeters announce your arrival?"

"No," Dr. Zenith said (soberly). "No, that will not be necessary."

"Shall I lead the way to the bonfire in the back, where Dr. Gurden and guests are enjoying their evening?"

"You may do so," Dr. Zenith gave a solemn nod.

I did. I led Dr. and Mrs. Zenith down the dark trail across the Gurden's back field to the bonfire, where Dr. Zenith presented Flash with Romulan Ale from the year 2283. "It's been reverse aged," we were informed.

Later, Amanda and I tried to figure out what Dr. Zenith had put into that blue Romulan Ale. I think complex molecular engineering was involved, possibly helped along by blue Curaçao liqueur and rum.

The truth is that Dr. Zenith is just a big Star Trek, Star Wars, Marvel Comics nerd who loves the sound of his own voice. And who blames him? I mean, really? He's an astrophysicist and he's wonderfully entertaining. That is, he's entertaining when he's not disgusted with me. And even then!

That 2010 fall semester, though... that fall semester I bore a large bull's-eye on my head, and Dr. Zenith delighted in pointing out any weakness ever I had.

I've had to change a couple of names in these books - to protect the guilty - but Dr. Zenith is a synonym for the man's real name. I've found in my life that people often do fit their names, as though we live in a children's story where the woman who rescues the stray cat is called Mrs. Goodkind, and Dr. Dastardly the cruel landlord declares, "You must pay the rent!" People are appropriately named in the real world too, from Dr. Cutting, my obstetrician, to Jack

Wisemore, campus pastor, to Ed Goodman, the gentlemanly young fellow who courted me in high school.

Dr. Zenith really is Dr. Zenith.

After all, a name should represent who you are.

CHAPTER 4

TROUBLESOME TRACKS

"To a dinosaur, a *Homo sapien* is known as 'food.'" - Dr. Stillwell

D r. Stillwell and I had developed a friendly sort of camaraderie during the spring of 2010. Then I stashed my dinosaur tracks in his lab. I'd asked Dr. Stillwell if I could bring the casts in for him to examine. I hadn't said, "Hey... these dinosaur prints really look like there are human prints with them." I hadn't said that. I wanted Dr. Stillwell to decide on his own what he thought they were.

But, still. I was just asking for disharmony by showing them to him at all.

Dr. Stillwell and I hadn't looked at the tracks together that spring. He got called off campus the last day I was in town, so I'd had to leave to Seattle with my casts still locked inside his lab. They sat tucked away under his rock saw table for the summer.

Despite all that, we started the fall semester merrily enough. I had signed up for Physical Geology, and I entered Dr. Stillwell's geology lab on the Tuesday after school started, arms filled with small boxes of coffee beans. My friend Michelle Caerphilly loved good coffee, just like my late husband. Randy had left a cupboard full of coffee beans from places like Guatemala and Ethiopia and Papua New Guinea.

Whitaker's eyes followed me as I stacked boxes on the black lab table. "Oooh. Coffee," he breathed the word with longing.

"I'll get you some," I assured big shaggy Whitaker, with his shaggy reddish brown hair and his shaggy reddish brown beard.

Randy's awesome cousin Carrie had married Whitaker, which made him my cousin by extension. Michelle Caerphilly had married Matthew Caerphilly's big brother Nathan. See? Everybody in West Virginia is related.

As I towered the exotic coffee beans at Michelle's spot, Dr. Stillwell's eyes glittered. "Hmmm," he tempted himself. "I might steal a box."

"I can give it to you," I said. "You don't have to steal it."

"No," Dr. S. said.

"Although, I know you do kipe things," I told him. "Like the occasional rock from a park."

"Oh, your memory is too good," he said. "And did you... did you really just use the word, 'kipe?'"

I left Dr. S. a box of coffee on his computer desk.

It just sat there.

Dr. Stillwell doesn't let people give him things. Ethics. Avoiding the appearance of evil. Something. He's not the beneficent emperor, you know. In the hall a few days later, I told Dr. Stillwell, "Look. That coffee is not a gift! It's payment for storing my dinosaur prints all summer."

He laughed and said he'd drink it, but the little box sat and sat and sat on his desk. For months.

I didn't know whether Dr. Stillwell had looked at the dinosaur prints. I didn't have to be there when he found them, though, and I think that was just as well. He could study them himself and decide what he thought they were without any input from me. They were casts made of real prints found in rock. My old boss Joe David had been at two of the digs where the prints were found. He had scrubbed the rock and made latex molds of the tracks. I had created casts from those original molds. Dr. Stillwell could think whatever he wanted to about the casts - but they were legitimate. Whatever they were – the tracks were real.

Everybody knows (everybody knows) humans and dinosaurs didn't live during the same time in Earth's history; their skeletal remains are buried in distantly separated layers. Jurassic and

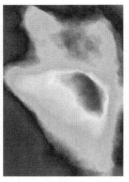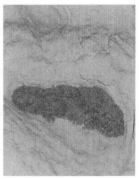

Figure 5 - "Girl Track" inside a theropod dinosaur track. Top left is the empty, plain track. Top right is the same track; the human-like print is filled with lentils. Middle and bottom are from a 3-D scan captured by the author using an XBox 360 Kinect, KScan3D 1.2 scanning software, and Foot Processor 1.20.3 (http://footprints. bournemouth.ac.uk/)

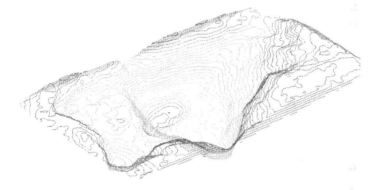

Cretaceous formations are situated far below the Pleistocene strata where we find human remains. Anybody who even suggests that dinosaurs and humans coexisted is seen as an uneducated moron. I could feel the open insults coming on.

On the other hand, we shouldn't expect to find human bones with dinosaur bones because they don't live in the same types of habitats - the same depositional environments. Dinosaurs often hung out in lower elevations, in the swampy areas along meandering rivers, while humans have tended to stay up on higher ground. Anything can take a walk down a river bed, but generally humans and dinosaurs wouldn't die in the same locations.

My problem was that I had these casts of prints from 110 million-year-old Cretaceous rock, and those prints looked like human footprints. They really did. I have no clue what alternate explanation would better explain the full range of geologic information. I just know my own foot fits the human-like print at the bottom of a three-toed *Acrocanthosaurus* track. That's it.

The tracks did turn things serious with Dr. Stillwell, of course. I knew they would. I walked into Dr. Stillwell's lab later that week, and I saw my casts set out right near the lab door. In other words, Dr. S. had found them - and he wanted them gone.

I gazed at them mournfully. "I'll get those out of here," I told him.

"I didn't throw them away," the geologist said, an evil something about his eyes. "They kept getting closer and closer to the door, but I didn't toss them out."

I nodded. "That was good of you."

"After all," he accused me, "you sneaked them in-"

"I asked you!" I reminded him. "You gave me permission!"

He frowned. "We were going to look at them. Why didn't we?"

"Because you kept having car trouble, and I had car trouble, and it didn't work out."

He wanted them gone? That was fine.

I grabbed the tracks and set the smaller ones up on the lab table. I showed him how my foot fit into the print at the bottom of the three-toed dino track. I noted how I could feel the pattern of her foot as it slid down into the lowest spot at the bottom. I pointed out the matching length and deep second digit of the other two human-like tracks. I puzzled about the cracks extending from the lower left side of both of them.

"They're just casts," I said.

"No, they're neat," Dr. Stillwell said. We stood by his lab door, but he didn't seem ready to chase me away. He suggested that they were made by something with human-like feet. He said that people had a tendency to see whatever they wanted to see.

It occurred to me later that he'd rather *invent* a creature with human-like feet, whatever that might be, than consider the possibility that I thought was more realistic - that humans had made human-shaped footprints.

I hauled the tracks out and stuck them back into my van. I didn't bother Dr. S. about them any more after that.

A few days later, Dr. Stillwell himself revisited the subject. I didn't fuss at him about it; he just brought it up on his own. The other students had filed out, and we walked toward the lab door, he and I. He paused before leaving. "Those tracks...they were interesting," he said politely.

His whole attitude irritated me. I didn't want that from him. I didn't like his polite façade, because inside his guts he didn't feel polite about my tracks at all.

"No, they're not interesting!" I insisted. "They're obnoxious. I don't want you to be nice, I want you to be straight with me. That's how we learn things. I'm not trying to prove anything, Dr. Stillwell," I told him. "But those footprints are a sticky note."

After a whole summer of waiting, I finally got his unbridled contempt. The real him. We both stood by the lab door while his face dropped its customary joviality, exposing the gray hardness underneath. "It's one of my pet peeves when people try to argue Creationism," he said.

"I know it is," I nodded.

"So, I finally stopped trying to argue with them. I just say, 'Go get yourself a graduate degree in geology and then come back and we can talk.'" His demeanor sharpened. "'Or get your *minister* to get a graduate degree in geology.'"

"Ahh," I thought. It's the result of too many students who just want to argue their pet ideas rather than figure out what's true.

Students. Please don't do that.

I didn't argue with him, because I had gotten what I wanted. I had gotten his honest response. Looking back, I wish I'd pressed it a bit more so I could get real answers from him - substantive arguments beyond his emotional irritation with creationists. After all, each of those human-like prints had a real explanation. They weren't carvings. They weren't frauds. They were casts made from latex molds - molds of tracks discovered when limestone was pulled up in front of dozens of witnesses. The fact that Dr. Stillwell wanted to throw them out just for existing... Well, that demonstrated his own bias.

I know we all have our biases, but whether they are popular or not, whether I *like* what I discover, I want to find the true answers to my questions.

CHAPTER 5

PEPSI V. RED BULL

I remember first reading about evolution in a book about dolphins when I was 10. The book said that dolphins had once been land mammals, and their legs had evolved into flippers over the years. I remember it clearly, reading that book on the carpet beside my bookshelf and thinking, "Wow. That's interesting. I didn't know that."

Encyclopedia Brown had already taught me that dinosaurs and men lived at different times, but I hadn't really heard the idea that one kind of animal had turned into a different kind of animal. It seemed perfectly reasonable to me at 10-years-old, and I don't remember a single person ever saying to me, "That isn't how it happened."

I learned about evolution through books and in high school biology. It wasn't addressed in either private or public schools otherwise. I don't remember a single sermon about evolution or creation in the Presbyterian church my father attended. I do remember the hymns and the zucchini bread and the rope swing outside under the cedar trees. We learned about cave men in my Lutheran grade school where they told us the earth was billions of years old. I don't recall any minister ever trying to convince me the earth was young. If there was any doubt in my mind, it came from the first chapter of Genesis itself. The Bible said the world was created in six days, and I didn't need a minister to point that out.

My mother moved us across the state to eastern Washington shortly after I turned 11. From then on we attended church only sporadically. It might be a Calvinist church or it might be a Methodist church or it might be no church at all. I did attend a Seventh Day Adventist school for Middle School, followed by a Jesuit high school and an Assembly of God college. When I lived in Texas, I spent every Sunday morning in the second pew from the front at the local Primitive Baptist church Joe David's family attended.

That right there is a jumble of doctrines. Ho boy. If you wanted to find four Christian denominations with the most varying, contrasting sets of beliefs, you might best choose Roman Catholic, Seventh Day Adventist, Assembly of God and Primitive Baptist. On the religious front, that's like moving a player from the Yankees to the Red Sox. It's like leaving Coke to work for Pepsi and ending up canning Red Bull.

The various churches did teach the same core doctrines of the Bible - that Jesus died to pay for our sins, that Jesus is God in the flesh, and that he rose again from the dead and ascended into Heaven. Despite the shared foundations, each denomination cherished doctrines that completely disagreed with the favorite doctrines of the others.

Primitive Baptists believe God chooses to save some people and not save others. They're serious about it. Assembly of God believers teach the free will of human beings to choose or reject God. Either way, God knows what will happen.

Seventh Day Adventists believe we should worship on Saturday - the seventh day - and resent the Roman Catholic Church for mandating Sunday as the day of rest. Many are vegetarians, while Catholics tend to freely consume both flesh and alcohol.

Catholics believe that when the priest blesses the elements of the Eucharist, they become the actual body and blood of Jesus Christ. Protestants reject the idea that Christ enters us because we eat something and insist that the Eucharist is an act of remembrance. (People have been executed over these disagreements!) Catholics believe Mary remained a virgin forever. Protestants think Joseph and Mary loved each other and had quite a few children after Jesus was born.

Catholic and Assembly of God and Seventh Day Adventist believers expect miracles and spiritual gifts for today's believers.

The Baptists are generally wary and even hostile toward spiritual gifts, arguing that healing and prophecy ceased after the time of the apostles.

I once told a faithful Primitive Baptist minister that God had instantly healed my herniated belly button when I was a baby, and that dear man tensed up. Why should my story make him feel uncomfortable? Didn't he believe in God and His power? Of course he did. He also believed that the gifts of the Spirit are *not for today,* and he had a self-built suspicion of instant-healing stories. I could appreciate his concerns about charlatans and snake charmers, but I had to disagree with his antagonism because I myself had been healed.

> *So they again called the man who was blind, and said to him, "Give God the glory! We know that this Man is a sinner." He answered and said, "Whether He is a sinner or not I do not know. One thing I know: that though I was blind, now I see."*
>
> John 9:24-25

The short of it is this: in every denomination I've visited, I've met people who live shiny lives filled with joy. In Catholic and Calvinist churches alike, I've met generous, kind people and I've met unpleasant twits. I've met both friendly and arrogant atheists too, for that matter. My loyalty cannot be to any one group, and it can't even be to "the decent people."[1]

As a young person, I didn't claim any denomination as my own. I figured I'd just honestly read the Bible and let it speak for itself, and I'd make my own decisions. Nobody was going to stand before God for me on the Day of Judgment. I was responsible for what I decided to believe. I wasn't trying to be self-important, I just needed to find out the answers for myself.

That attitude didn't stop with questions of faith - it spread into every subject I studied.

I'm keenly aware that there are multiple sides to every story in this world, and I try to suspend judgment about a person or place

---

1   For the record, I do note that there's a difference between people who are just friendly and people who are filled with the comforting and satisfying presence of the Holy Spirit. I recognize that difference now, and it's almost tangible.

or issue until I've given it a thorough look. Don't worry if I hear nasty rumors about you. I probably won't believe them until I see some proof.

I'm also keenly aware that people hang onto their views. We humans are emotionally attached to our beliefs - atheists and evangelicals alike - and because I am aware of it, I work hard to avoid making emotional decisions. The true answer isn't always the one that feels good. It's not always the one that is familiar or comfortable or easy. The true answer... is whatever it is.

So. Evolution.

I told Dr. Stillwell one day, "If God wanted to use evolution to make the spectrum of life on earth, then that's fine. What's it to me how He did it?" Dr. S. nodded in agreement when I said it. Maybe God set up this world so that all life could evolve from amino acids floating around in the sea like biochemistry professor Dr. Manchester believed. Maybe the Lord organized and fine-tuned the world so that biological organisms could self-form, and He just wound up the cosmos and let it go.

On the other hand, maybe God actually created groups of animals fully formed at the beginning like the Bible says, and the different groups evolved into a wide variety of species and subspecies as they meandered across the world. What predictions can we make from either position, and which predictions match what we see?

The agenda should be to figure out what's true. If two people who both care about true answers put their heads together, then the fact that they have different perspectives is a good thing. I have the perspective that God is real, but I also look at the geologic evidence that I have - and I'm trying to interpret it correctly.

Honestly, I do not see a drooling rainbow of intermediary forms in the fossil record. We should expect a multitude of intermediate forms over the long 540 million years since the Cambrian started. Niles Eldredge and Stephen Jay Gould famously suggested that evolutionary changes take place primarily in small subpopulations, and they thought we should see the stable fossils and not all the short-lived versions in between. I appreciate their honest ideas.

However, I'm less convinced that they've answered the problem the longer I think about it. If most of the history of life involves evolutionary change from common ancestors, we should still see a host of intermediate forms converging into a trunk as we go backward in time - like the fictitious caminalcules in the image below.[2]

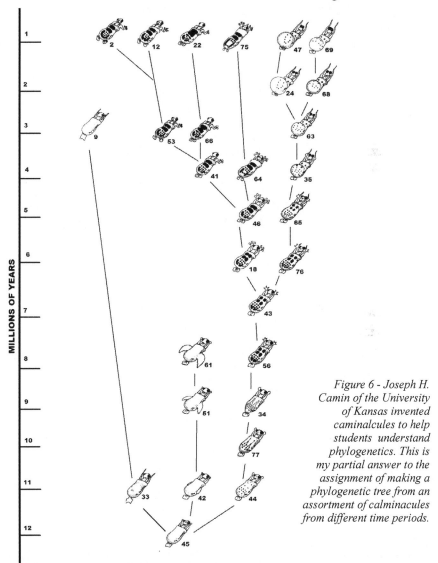

Figure 6 - Joseph H. Camin of the University of Kansas invented caminalcules to help students understand phylogenetics. This is my partial answer to the assignment of making a phylogenetic tree from an assortment of calminacules from different time periods.

2   Cf. Gendron, R.P (2000) The Classification & Evolution of Caminalcules. *The American Biology Teacher*, 62(8):570-576.

The caminalcules produce a series of subsequent forms, and they represent what we'd expect from Darwinian evolution. However, that's not what we find in the rocks.

Instead, we find that distinct forms have existed from the beginning of the fossil record.[3] The Burgess Shale in British Columbia provides us with a multitude of Cambrian phyla, including soft body parts, all well-formed and not in the least connected to each other. Trilobites with their incredible compound eyes - boom - just appear, along with sponges and brachiopods and annelid worms and corals. The Precambrian Ediacaran fossils, which have given paleontologists hope as ancestors of the Cambrian fauna, have proved disappointing after all.

Richard Fortey wrote in *Science* in 2001:

> The beginning of the Cambrian period, some 545 million years ago, saw the sudden appearance in the fossil record of almost all the main types of animals (phyla) that still dominate the biota today. To be sure, there are fossils in older strata, but they are either very small (such as bacteria and algae), or their relationships to the living fauna are highly contentious, as is the case with the famous soft-bodied fossils from the late Precambrian Pound Quartzite, Ediacara, South Australia.[4]

Even articles that do their best to offer a connection between Ediacaran and Cambrian biota admit there's painfully little to work with. In a 2015 paper, Mary Droser and James Gehling repeatedly noted the trouble with tying Ediacaran forms to Cambrian fauna, resorting to the position that Ediacaran fauna shared the most basic characteristics with Cambrian animals, like mobility, sexual reproduction and skeletonization.[5] Even if the Ediacaran organisms enjoyed these extremely general traits (which is questionable), it's obvious there is little to establish a direct relationship between the Ediacaran fauna and Cambrian life.

---

3   Stephen Meyer's 2013 book *Darwin's Doubt* describes this issue in great detail.
4   Fortey, R. (2001). The Cambrian Explosion Exploded? *Science*, 293(5529):438-439.
5   Droser, M.L. & Gehling, J.G. (2015). The Advent of Animals: The View from the Ediacaran. *PNAS*, 112(16):4865-4870.

When we look at the fossil record, we don't see a tree. Instead, we see bushy shrubs. At least, that's what I see. I see shrubs with only an exceptionally rare, speculative intermediate. There is a horse shrub with bushy branches of Miohippus and Mesohippus, zebras and onagers and Clydesdales and Black Beauty. There is a shrub branching out with camels of various sizes, and there is a shrub of trilobites. A shrub can be a phylum, like Brachiopoda, or it can be a family, like Felidae, the "cat family." Remember, our classification schemes are just our best efforts to organize life on Earth. They were invented by us. However, while we find a variety of different horses or camels or trilobites or brachipods, we don't find the multitude of intermediates that were supposed to have connected them all together at different points in history. And I see that as a problem. If we have the bushy ends of the branches, we should also have the sturdy branches that led to them. We'd expect to be missing some intermediates, certainly, but intermediates should still make up a significant part of the fossil record - and they don't.

But see, that's my perspective. I wanted to be able to talk honestly with Dr. Stillwell and get his perspective - his additional knowledge that extended beyond what I knew. I didn't want to argue with him. I wanted to share notes.

That's why Dr. Stillwell's reaction to the footprints aggravated me. It didn't bother me that he said, "People see what they want to see." That is an absolutely true statement. It bothered me that he just dismissed the tracks the way he did. Wrist-flick. I knew that he had 35 years of geological experience under his belt, and that experience told him that dinosaurs had died out 63 million years before humankind showed up. I recognized that. But those tracks still required an explanation.

I had collected a few grievances with Dr. Stillwell by that point. Mostly, I still hadn't gotten to ask all the questions festering in my guts. The geology professor frustrated me. I wanted to put everything on the table and discuss issues, to excavate his brain and collect his insights. I wanted to criticize him for making judgments based on assumptions, for his bad habit of jumping to conclusions. I wanted to have a real conversation with him without its descending into a political rant.

"Okay, Lord," I said. "Can I have it out with Dr. Stillwell?"

The answer came pretty quickly.

"No," He said. "Be quiet."

CHAPTER 6

UNTIL THE FIRE BURNS

D r. Stillwell's attitude over the dinosaur tracks had been hostile and harsh and I wanted to find out what made him so sure about his position. I wanted to confront him and talk it out. When I prayed about it, though, I was told to back off. The answer I got through Davidian poetry stated, "Shhh Amy Joy. Just hush for a bit:"

I was mute with silence, I held my peace even from good;
And my sorrow was stirred up. My heart was hot within me;
While I was musing, the fire burned. Then I spoke with my
tongue.

Psalm 39:2-3

I sighed. "Okay, Lord."[1]

That was August 24, just over a week into the new school year.

I agreed. I had wanted to confront Dr. S., but I agreed to keep quiet. I made the decision to hold my peace for a time, something I'm not good at even a little bit. It was a wise thing for me to just keep my mouth closed - at least until "the fire burned" and God released me to speak.

Normally, I don't get answers right away. I can ask God questions and hear no answer for weeks or months beyond a simple, "Be patient," or "Trust me." When I asked questions about Dr. Stilllwell, though, the answer would pop out almost instantly, which is precisely

---

1   Let's say I was wrong, and it was all just in my head. Is there any *harm* in shutting up for a little bit? Does it contradict the major teachings of Jesus, things like "love your neighbor", "love your enemy", "go two miles with a man who asks you to go one mile", "humble yourself?" No.

why I'm writing this book. That August, I asked the Lord if I could confront Dr. Stillwell, and He immediately told me to keep quiet. It made me wonder, "What is the deal? Why is this geology professor so important?"

Don't you know, that next day in class I couldn't answer a single one of Dr. Stillwell's questions? I had already planned to keep my mouth shut, but that day I simply had no answers. I tend to be an encyclopedia when I'm around Dr. Stillwell, and that day I wasn't.

The geology professor noticed too. I lent him a pen to sign something for another student, and after he scribbled out his name, he handed it back to me. I took the pen in my fingers, but he wouldn't release it on his end. The good doctor and I stood there for a few seconds, each holding one end of the innocent writing utensil.

"How are you doing today, Amy Joy?" he asked. "You're being awfully quiet."

I shrugged. "I'm just trying to be nice." I tugged on my pen again, and he let go.

"You're always nice," Dr. Stillwell said.

"Noooo, I'm not always gneiss," I rock punned. "Actually, sometimes I'm a bit of a schist."

Dr. Stillwell laughed out loud, a cheerful sound.

"Oh, you've heard that a thousand times," I grinned.

"Yes," he said, "But you did it so well!"

I didn't linger. I headed out of the lab.

For the next week, I did my best to avoid any conversations with Dr. Stillwell, even simple ones. Matthew and I bumped into him outside one day, and I said, "Oh hi, Dr. S." I introduced him and Matthew to each other. Then Dr. Stillwell went one way and we went another. We bumped into the professor again in the hallway of the science building half a minute later.

"Doh!" I said. "We were trying to avoid you!"

I meant it lightly, but a film of hurt crossed Dr. Stillwell's eyes.

That week the Environmental Department held its annual picnic out in the courtyard in front of the science building, and the first floor professors flipped veggie burgers and handed out chips and pop. I sat in the grass and chattered with my fellow students. I didn't speak to Dr. S. even once.

It grieved me not to banter with the good doctor on short walks down the hall. I enjoyed our occasional chats and found I had a difficult time ignoring him. We had a Physical Geology camping trip approaching in two weeks, and I hated the thought of having to wait until then to talk things through with the professor. In the meanwhile, I'd stand and argue with him in the mirror at home, completely wasting time late at night when I should have been doing homework.

Toward the beginning of the next week, my heart started to burn in me. It burned away, a pleasant feeling that gave me hope. It's a comforting fire that I've always liked, but I never know what to do with it. Somebody once told me it was the anointing of the Holy Spirit, but the burning is never accompanied by ideas or extra wisdom or instructions. It's just a nice, pleasant fire in my chest. I believe it's the same burning mentioned in Luke 24:32 by the men who had walked with Jesus on the road to Emmaus. At this point, I simply had to wait until God opened the door for a real conversation with Dr. Stillwell.

"Lord, I don't want to do this anymore," I groaned one day in the school hallway. "How much longer do I have to wait?"

Wednesday, September 1st, I plugged my nearly-dead cell phone into the wall of the geology lab at the beginning of class. Later that morning, I realized I had left my phone behind, and as soon as class let out I ran back to the geology lab to grab it. I tried the door, but Dr. Stillwell had already locked up and left. Darn.

I'd have to visit Dr. Stillwell's office to see if he'd let me into his classroom. I marched down to the end of the hall, turned the corner and then looked up. Dr. Zenith appeared ahead of me, standing just inside Dr. Stillwell's open office door. Oh man. I didn't even pause; I just walked on by the two men. My phone could wait.

"Hey, Amy Joy!" Dr. Stillwell hollered as I passed. "Did you leave your cell phone and charger in my lab?"

Reluctantly, I stopped and returned to his doorway. "Yes, I did," I admitted.

"Well, we'll go down in a minute and get it," he said.

Dr. Zenith frowned. "I wouldn't give them to her," he said the words evenly, with no hint of humor. "I would give them away or I would throw them away."

I stood there in the doorway, not speaking, not moving, just staring down at Dr. Stillwell's desk. Dr. Zenith always made me feel like a small child who'd just had her hand smacked.

"All right. I'll see you at the meeting at three," Dr. Zenith told his colleague. Then he passed by me and strode off down the hall. He didn't even want to share oxygen with me.

Dr. S. gazed up, compassion warming his eyes. "Oh, don't mind him," he urged. "Come on! Sit down and talk to me!"

The heavy weight of waiting dropped off my heart with a rejoicing thump. I slid into the chair by Dr. Stillwell's door, utterly relieved to end my week of being mum. There was a physical element to it, the lifting of misery from my soul.

Looking back, the whole thing is just bizarre. I was the annoying chick that brought in controversial dinosaur track casts. I'm the one who answered questions about Noah's Ark. This geologist should not have been urging me to sit in his office for a friendly talk.

"It's okay. I love Dr. Zenith," I told my professor as I settled into my seat. "He's great. And here's a secret something about Amy Joy. I'm really deep down in my soul 10-years-old. So, I don't mind it. He keeps me humble."

"No," Dr. Stillwell disagreed. He looked at me through his glasses, his eyes extra big. (Whenever I think of conversations between us and remember his abnormally large eyes, I realize that he must have been wearing his glasses.) "No. You're 12. Fourteen is too old, 10 is too young. I think you're 12."

I laughed inside myself. He understood me.

"Don't - don't run away," he urged me. "Stay here for a few minutes and talk to me."

I did. For nearly an hour we sat there and talked and talked and talked, and nobody interrupted us. I heard stories about Dr. Stillwell's mother and a bit about his growing up on a dairy farm on the Olympic Peninsula. He asked me about my family, and I filled him in.

I explained that my brother Lex had left when I was nine and my mother moved me across the state from my father two years later, and those losses had made holes in my heart. That was my most fundamental issue. Yes, my husband had died the previous September, but losing Randy only added to my deeper struggle, which is that my big brother and father had been misplaced for me at a young age.

"Tell me about your family," Dr. Stillwell urged me. So I did. I described my seven brothers and sisters and I told him about my parents and my grandparents and basically gave him an introduction to the life of Amy Joy.

At one point in our long getting-to-know-you session, I growled about not letting anybody tell me what to think, and Dr. Stillwell chuckled.

"Have you seen *The Life of Brian?*" he asked.

"It's Monty Python, right?" I said.

Dr. Stillwell nodded. "Yes, it's all about Brian, and he goes through life just a regular guy, but eventually people start thinking he's the Messiah, and at one point he's before this crowd and they want to listen to what he has to say. He's trying to get them to understand he's not the Messiah. He's saying, 'No, you don't need to follow me. You need to think for yourselves. You are all individuals.' And they're all chanting, 'We're all individuals.' And he's saying, 'No, you're all different. You need to be different.' And they're all saying, "We're all different. We're all different.' And in the back one guy says, 'I'm not.'"

We both started laughing. I have never seen the film, but that part had its charm.

"I think that's you," he said. "'I'm not!'"

During our Grand Canyon trip the next May, I fell behind our group because I wanted to snap some pictures of my fellow student Jared sitting at the edge. I'd taken three shots when Dr. Stillwell retraced his steps and grabbed me. Literally. He took firm hold of my backpack strap and tugged me along, hissing into my ear, "I don't have to talk to you about *The Life Of Brian* again, do I?"

I grinned. No, sir.

Dr. Stillwell didn't grab Jared or threaten Jared for going too near the edge. That's because Jared was a dude. With tattoos. Who worked as a river rafting guide and played lead guitar in a rock band. Dr. Stillwell never once grabbed Jared by the backpack.

Figure 7 - Jared on the South Rim.

We had a fun talk that September day, Dr. Stillwell and I, and we both got a chance to tell each other stories.

"My first job was working as a dishwasher at Gloria's Steakhouse in Prichard, Idaho when I was 15," I said at one point.

"Prichard!" he exclaimed. "You miss it if you blink! I used to do a lot of geology work out there in the '70s."

"Yeah, I'd get done with work around midnight, drenched from neck to knees. I'd stand outside and watch the bats catch bugs under the big streetlight over the parking lot." That was one of the many unique things about living in the wilderness. A river flowed west just 100 yards away. Elk lived in the field behind the steakhouse. At the same time, we lived in a trailer no bigger than a 5th wheel, with just a kitchenette, a bed, and a tiny bathroom. It was cramped at night for my mother and six kids. (Lex was gone, and Jordan hadn't yet been born.)

"After work, I'd go down into the little camping trailer where we were living behind the steak house," I told Dr. Stillwell. "I'd try to find a place to sleep. But, the bed was taken, and the little foldout couch was filled, and there were kids sleeping on all the floor space, and there would be no place for me to lie down."

I tried sleeping on the hay bales out back, but the bales were stiff and the straws stuck into me. I tried sleeping in the forts my brothers had dug out of the sand piles in the parking lot, but sand is hard and cold. I wouldn't have minded camping outside, but there were no extra blankets or sleeping bags to use.

Dr. Stillwell listened with lively interest. These things were part of my life's adventure, and he'd had adventures of his own.

"Finally, the old lady who lived next door to us offered me a mattress on her floor. And I'll tell you what," I told Dr. Stillwell, "I felt like the luckiest, most comfortable person ever. The other kids were still squishing onto the little couch while I slept like a queen on Imogene's living room floor."

I think that entertained the good doctor.

Dr. Stillwell told about working in Seattle as a young adult. He'd had men pull guns on him when he worked as a store clerk. One night, a would-be thief approached him from behind with a frozen hunk of meat. Young Paul Stillwell saw the meat-wielder in a glass door reflection, and as the guy raised the package to deck him, Paul spun around and throat punched him. He's feisty, Dr. Stillwell is.

"There is something dangerous in you," I told him during a particularly serious moment. I wasn't joking around. It was something I had noticed. "I don't know what it is, but I see it once in awhile, and I know I don't want to touch whatever it is."

His face sobered when I said that. "I've lived several lives," he said, "and the life I have now is good and pleasant, and I believe I'm here for the duration." I didn't think his other lives involved running drugs or murder or CIA work in Rwanda, but you never know.

That September day in his office, my professor came around his wall again. He generally protected his privacy and maintained a careful professionalism, but that day he had some things he wanted to say to me, and eventually he said them. Personal things. Things I don't think he'd normally share.

"I look at you," he gazed at me intently, "and it's clear that you've lived a more serious life than most of the other students."

I shook my head. "A lot of people have horrible stuff happen." Horrible things. Much worse than anything I've gone through.

"No, that's not the point," he said. "While some people are sitting there, upset about their *hangnails*," he stressed the word, "you are dealing with some really huge issues. I think you're doing better this semester than the last one, but sometimes you would come into the room and I could see you were handling some weighty matters in your life."

I appreciated that. I truly appreciated that he could see me, that he could look past my folded arms as I stared at his PowerPoint screen. He could see me for *me*. I appreciated his willingness to notice, to come out from behind his wall and relate to me without the normal protective tarp people wrap around their lives.

Dr. S. finally let me go. We both had other classes to attend, but I left his office that morning completely elated and at peace. In that hour, we had passed an official boundary into friendship, and it rejoiced my heart. And I hadn't brought up geology even once.

At the same time, the whole thing befuddled me. Why did God speak to me so quickly and firmly about Dr. Stillwell?

"Don't argue with him."

"He's my business, not yours."

"Don't rebuke an older man, but entreat him as a father."

"Keep your mouth closed, even from good, until your heart burns, and then you can speak."

When I asked God questions about Dr. S., I always received immediate responses. You know what? About the time I had gotten aggravated with the good doctor, I'd been asking, "Lord, where's my wallet? Please help me find my wallet."

Nothing. Not a peep from the Holy Spirit about my wallet.

I didn't know that somebody had turned it in to campus police, and all I had to do was check my email. That wasn't the point. The point was that I had asked and asked about my wallet - which was fairly important to me, by the way - and I hadn't gotten a response. It's not like God can't tell me where my wallet is. Wallets and keys and cell phones aren't too small for the God of the Universe. He's helped me find things before.

As soon as I asked about Dr. Stillwell, though - bam - I got an answer.

I have often wondered about it. What is the deal with Dr. Stillwell? Why is he so important? More specifically, why was it so important that I not screw up my relationship with him? Because I'm perfectly capable of screwing up relationships. It's that whole mind-to-mouth filter problem I have.

I finally concluded that Dr. Stillwell was a minefield. He was a minefield, and my asking questions like, "What if there really *was* a global Flood? Would it look any different than what we see?" - that might have damaged the whole comfort level thing we'd been developing. I mean, after four years I *still* haven't gotten to ask him that question, and I keep wanting to. What's the big deal! He could give me added perspective!

There might be some huge, eternal import in my having a friendship with this geology professor. Maybe. On the other hand, it might be something so simple as God's filling that hole I'd had those many long years since Lex left. And…maybe… just maybe the old geology prof had his own holes that needed plugging. The thought of that all by itself has often brought tears to my eyes.

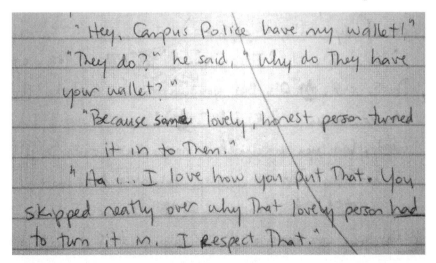

"Hey, Campus Police have my wallet!"
"They do?" he said, "Why do They have your wallet?"
"Because some lovely, honest person turned it in to Them."
"Ha ... I love how you put That. You skipped neatly over why That lovely person had to turn it in. I Respect That."

Figure 8 - From my journal, dated September 4, 2010 - a light-hearted exchange with the good doctor.

CHAPTER 7
THE DROWNING OF TROY

"If a data point lands on the line, use it. If Heaven drops you a plum, open your mouth. I believe in a kind and merciful Heaven." - Dr. Zenith

Writing book manuscripts takes time, and life continues during the writing of them. Since starting this tale, I have moved 2500 miles across the country and taken charge of a chemistry lab. Right now I am in the process of buying a house, and I'd like to sell my conversion van - as soon as we can stop it from leaking coolant. I've taken in two cats and my grandfather has died.

Dr. Stillwell called me two days ago and we had a wonderfully fun chat about crayfish and bryozoan expert Crazy Ernie. The story keeps moving forward, even while these pages have hardly caught you up to September 2010.

Today is Sunday, the 21st of July, 2013. My brother Baron called me this afternoon while I was at the grocery store with my two young sons.

"Did I tell you about the boy who drowned on the river yesterday?" he asked.

"No!" I said. "Where on the river? By the Rock?"

"Right there by the swimming hole."

"Our swimming hole?" I asked.

"Yes," Baron said. "Our swimming hole."

"What happened?" I asked. "The boy died?"

"Yes he died," Baron said. "But you need to hear the whole story. And it all started because Drew got drunk."

Because Drew got drunk.

Baron is a surveyor these days, and on Friday his surveying partner Drew came to work more than a little hung over. As a result of Drew's deteriorated condition, he and Baron didn't get their work done, which meant they'd have to go out on Saturday to finish up.

Baron's cheer meter dropped into the red. Not only would he have to work without pay on a beautiful summer Saturday morning, but he wouldn't get to take his 8-year-old foster son fishing on Rose Lake as planned. Mom watched young Lance for Baron, which meant that Baron had to go up to our family ranch after work to get the little guy.

When Baron finally got to the Ranch after work, Lance decided he didn't want to go fishing after all. Baron thought he'd go up to the Rock to go swimming, but Mom interrupted that plan too. "Jordan and Guy are going down to the swimming hole. Why don't you go with them?"

"Okay," Baron said. "We can take my truck."

These are all important details. Baron had to be at the Ranch to get Lance. He decided to go with our sister Jordan and (ranch hand) Guy to the swimming hole. They drove down to the swimming hole in Baron's truck.

"We'd been at the swimming hole just a little bit when these people floated by on tubes," Baron spoke through the phone as I pushed a cart past apples and oranges. "They had a boy with them about ten-years-old. We watched them float by, and then we didn't notice anything until we heard them screaming a few minutes later down at the log jam."

Jordan is our youngest sister, and when her father died, he left the Ranch to her. Technically it's Jordan's property. The river bends around the far side of her land there, about a quarter mile past the swimming hole, and the spring floods always leave a big mess of logs down at the bend. The Forest Service has cleared the log jam in the past, but every year it gets loaded up again.

"The yelling down at the log jam continued for a few minutes," Baron said. He and Jordan kept looking downriver, trying to figure out what was going on.

Jordan later told me, "At first we thought they were just playing a game. They were yelling and running into the river and out of the river. We sat for a long time watching them. Then this guy starts screaming like he's in pain, and I thought he'd hurt himself playing the game."

The man's screams sounded serious. Baron swam back across the river and put on his shirt. He pulled on his boots and laced them up. Baron could have covered a quarter mile in 90 seconds if he were on the road, but the semi-jungle beside the river slowed him down and several minutes passed as he navigated it. He trekked through the heavy, tall grass along the river bank, avoiding hidden pits and downed logs, heading to where he thought this shrieking man had injured himself.

It turned out the man wasn't injured. He and his buddy had been trying to save the boy from drowning.

"It took forever for me to get there," Baron said.

I could almost hear my brother shaking his head on the phone.

He continued, "By the time I reached the log jam, there was the sense that everybody had given up. The boy's tube had flipped over. He'd gotten caught under the water by his lifejacket. All that time they'd been running in and out, and the time the guy was screaming, and the time it took me to swim across the river and lace up my boots and get down there, the little boy had been hooked on the branches under the water with the river rushing into his face. When I reached them, they had just finished cutting the boy free. They weren't even hurrying at this point."

The boy's name was Troy. His father had spent a tragic, fruitless struggle to free his son from the power of all that water pulling the boy under the water, hooked on the tangled branches of the log jam. The river had ripped the father away from the child again and again, tearing the clothes off their bodies. After the third or fourth effort, the father had started screaming. It was those sounds of helpless grief that made Baron finally go investigate - screams of pain and despair because the man couldn't save his son. The life jacket was new. They couldn't free it from the branches, and they couldn't undo the new, stiff fasteners.

The father tried again and again. He finally swam above Troy, floated downstream and caught hold of him long enough to cut him free from the shackles of his life vest. One of their friends grabbed Troy as he was being washed downstream, just as Baron jogged across the river rocks to the shore. Worn down by his own battle against the water, the man handed the lifeless body into Baron's arms.

"How did it make you feel when he gave you this dead kid?" I asked my brother. Baron had served in Kosovo and Iraq. He'd seen death.

"A dozen things go through your mind at that moment," Baron said. "'Please don't be dead. Gosh, kid. You really look dead. Don't be dead. God, don't let him be dead.' He was all grayed out. His face had no color. His pupils were completely dilated. His eyes were wide open and staring into nothing. He was just this cold floppy thing in my arms."

Baron bellowed as loudly as he could back at Jordan, "Get my truck!!" Jordan had hiked about halfway to the log jam, so she turned and shouted the message up to Guy. There was no cell phone service up in those mountains, no chance of calling 911 without a landline. Guy just needed to find a way to get the truck down there.

Baron carried the white, bloodless boy to the shore and handed him to his mother. She lay him on the rocks and began slapping his chest and stomach. It became rapidly clear that nobody on the shore knew what to do.

Baron stepped back in and took charge. He began to do CPR on Troy, surrounded by the child's grieving family. "And while I'm doing CPR I'm trying to pray for him, but the only thing I can pray is, 'Jesus, you love him. You love him. Jesus, you *love* him.' At one point there was gurgling in the boy's lungs, and his family said, 'He's breathing? He's alive!' And I said, 'No. No, he's not alive.'

It was just my air bubbling through the water in his lungs. He wasn't breathing. He still had no pulse."

Breathe. Breathe. Pump. Pump. Pump. Pump. Pump… "Jesus, you love him. Jesus, you love him."

In the meanwhile, Guy hiked back to Baron's big old Chevy truck. Guy is the handyman on the property. We always introduce him as, "This is Guy, the guy who lives in the barn." He's a faithful old gentleman who helps train the horses and mow the grounds and mend fences and fight off the vicious rooster when he goes to collect eggs. When Jordan relayed Baron's message, Guy made his way back to Baron's truck and drove it around the long way on the other side of the woods, over the rocks to the shore by the log jam. Jordan's car would never have made it through the bumpy fields and along the river bank.

"Then Troy started breathing," Baron said. "They were shallow breaths, but he did start breathing on his own. His eyes were still staring at nothing, but he started breathing." He didn't choke up water, though; he still had water in his lungs.

As soon as Guy came bumping over the rocks, Baron carried Troy over and set him in the cab. The boy's father got in and held him. Guy wasted no time. He drove back over the rocky shore, past the trees and across the property and up to the house where he called 911. Then he raced down the River Road, speeding at 75-80 miles-per-hour.

"The sheriff passed me and threw on his lights," Guy later told me. "But, I wasn't stopping." The sheriff had heard about the situation on the radio, and he just followed Guy. On the way down the river, Troy's father kept telling the boy, "Squeeze my hand. Keep breathing and stay awake. It's okay. Keep breathing."

They met up with the ambulance at about the five-mile marker on the River Road. When the EMT took Troy, the first thing he did was check the child's blood oxygen level. Guy said it didn't even register on the equipment. Still, Baron's CPR had been enough. As soon as they put him on oxygen, the boy yelled and thrashed around, as though his brain thought he was still under the water. The EMTs closed the back door, and the ambulance wailed off to the hospital.

"It was like a big divinely-appointed relay," Baron said. "The man handed Troy to me, and I did CPR on him just long enough to hand him to Guy, who sped down the River Road and handed him to the EMTs, who raced him to the hospital."

As Baron was telling me this, I warded off my own sons from dropping cookies and microwave popcorn into the grocery cart.

"I found out he'd ended up at Sacred Heart in Spokane," Baron said. "I called the hospital today and asked about him. They said, 'We can't talk to you about patients, but his father is standing right here. You can talk to him.' Troy's dad got on the phone, and he said, 'He's awake and talking, and right now we're watching television.'"

"Really?" I laughed. "That's so great!"

You know what? After relaying Baron's message to Guy, Jordan swam across the river to the dirt road on the other side. She managed to stop a pickup truck and say, "They need help down there. They're screaming. Would you drive over there really quickly and see what's wrong?" The driver refused. "I'm on my way to my camp," he said. "Please," Jordan begged him, "I think somebody is seriously hurt." The man shrugged her off and just drove away.

That man would have let a little 10-year-old boy die. He didn't know what was going on, but that's not the point. He didn't *care*. If Baron had not been willing to investigate - if he had gone fishing at Rose Lake - it seems certain Troy would have stayed dead. But, Baron was there. He was there, because he'd had to work that day, because Drew got drunk.

"So, we're going to have a barbeque for them up at the Ranch," Baron finished his story on the phone. He asked me, "Do you want to come?"

"Yeah, I want to come to the barbeque!" I said. I chased my six-year-old off the top of the kids' cart I was pushing. "I want to meet Troy! That will be so cool."

Post Script:

A month later, Troy's parents returned to the Ranch, where we ate and had a good time. Troy had no memory of the scariest parts of that day, and he seemed perfectly calm as we sat and talked about it. His parents said he didn't demonstrate signs of brain damage, except for maybe a tendency to be absent minded. (Which, isn't every 10-year-old absent minded?) Shortly after the drowning, Troy's grandfather called Baron and promised him a bottle of scotch, so Troy's parents brought the scotch up to Baron. He hasn't touched it. It's a constant reminder that even lousy situations can be for the good.

"I was just a little cog in this big machinery that was put in place to save Troy's life," Baron said. "And God was willing to inconvenience me in order to do something so much better than what I had planned."

Figure 9 - The log jam that Troy overcame.

CHAPTER 8

BARON

At 14 years of age, Baron had an encounter with the presence of God that changed him forever. For two hours he lay pinned on the floor of Coeur d'Alene Christian Center, unable to get up. He said it felt like a giant palm pressed on his chest and arms, as though God Himself held him down. It wasn't just that Baron couldn't get up. Big men lost the battle to pull Baron's skinny 115-pound body off the carpet. Anybody who tried fell down. Two hours. Baron wasn't just hallucinating or having a seizure; nobody could move him.

"I was thinking about that last night," Baron said to me in my living room just now. "I was thinking that if I had been watching that as an outsider, I'd have thought, 'Well. This is weird.'"

I'm laughing at my silly brother as I type out what he said.

It was certainly a unique event in our lives. Nothing like that had happened in that church before, and nothing like it happened after that either, as far as I know.

During those two hours, Baron was overwhelmed by the presence of God. He had glimpses of Heaven, and God spoke to him and told him good things about our family, things that Baron would never have expected, things that started coming true within just a few years.

"I love you, Baron," God said. "You're going to Heaven. Your whole family is going to Heaven." Those were important words for Baron. Those were important words for our whole shaken and bruised family.

Baron went on to join the Army at age 19. He served in Kosovo and Iraq. He later became a tower climber, hand-over-handing it up 2000-foot-high communication towers to repair the light bulbs at the top. After that, he entered the mines, drilling holes in the earth a mile under the ground. Despite his life experiences, Baron has never felt able to adequately describe the power and love and security of the presence of God using any earthly comparisons.

Figure 10 - Baron in a communications tower in 2010. Those are tree-covered hills behind him. Photo by Joey Hall.

Sometimes Baron has been a model Christian, and sometimes he just plain hasn't been. He's a normal, red blooded man who faces the same struggles all men face. While living in Seattle at one point in his life, he made one of the worst choices of all time.

"People had offered me every kind of drug in the world, and I'd always said no," Baron explained to me. "There were drugs everywhere you went. 'Hey man. Hey man, you want something?' This kid got off the bus downtown, and he went to go buy himself a Mountain Dew. When he got back he said, 'Wow. I just got offered crack for the first 15 times in my life.'"

Baron had moved to Seattle with the idea of helping people, but it just plain ended badly. He told me, "It got pretty easy to identify which people were addicted to different drugs. If they looked sick, they were coming off of heroin. If they looked like they'd just gotten out of a concentration camp, they were on meth. Everybody knew I didn't do drugs, but one night this one guy Jay kept offering and offering and offering something to me, and I was curious so I finally gave in and tried it. I had no clue. It turns out it was meth, which is like the worst drug ever. I binged for the next five days. I didn't eat. I didn't sleep."

By the end of the week Baron had lost a ton of weight as his starving body ate away at itself. His eyes sunk in from lack of water. He was killing himself. "And when you do meth," he told me, "it's so obvious to everybody around you. You're trying so hard to walk normally and look normal, but there's no being normal on it."

Baron knew it was going to kill him, but the desire to use was more powerful than the desire to live. He stood at a free pay phone by the bus station in Seattle for an hour, staring at the pay phone, trying to make a decision. He was going to call his supplier. That was certain. But he also knew he should call Dad. If he called Dad first, Dad might come. If he called his supplier first, he wouldn't call Dad, and he would fry his brain. It was a horrible, painful decision. Baron finally picked up the phone, and Dad drove into Seattle and got him.

Baron looked like a shell of himself when our sister Heather saw him at Dad's place. Baron's eyes were sunken and his skin smelled like urine. Horrified, Heather took him home with her and nursed him and gave him detoxing remedies to get the stuff out of his system. "She saved my life," Baron insists. "I don't care what Heather has ever done wrong, I will be eternally grateful to her for saving my life." Baron left Seattle after that and came out to live with me in West Virginia for awhile.

Methamphetamine is a devastatingly addictive drug. It causes the brain to dump the neurotransmitter dopamine into the system, releasing the "pleasure" chemical in super high amounts and giving the user a feeling of invincibility. Baron said to me, "I think meth is a poison, and it makes the brain think you're dying, so it dumps all its resources into helping you escape this terrible situation you're in."

I wondered about that. I asked Baron, "When you were 14, was your experience with *God* like a meth high?"

"No," Baron shook his head. "No. Meth is called the 'devil's drug' for a reason. It makes you feel powerful and amazing, but you also think it would be cool to rip an old lady to shreds and eat the pieces. It's like, anything hideous inside you gets magnified and you think that evil is awesome. God's love is the opposite. It's clean and pure."

Baron looked at me earnestly. "You know how you go up a tall roller coaster, and there's that moment when you go over the lip of the roller coaster, and you see down?" he tried to explain.

"That's what God's love is like. But, we're not talking about a scary ride here, we're talking about a really good feeling. It's so intense, it feels like being electrocuted. Super powerful, but it doesn't hurt at all. Then pretend that anybody that you ever really loved, people you've lost, suddenly walked into the room. Now, think of that great book, the greatest book you've ever read, when you finish it, you still don't want to put it down, you want to pick it up and start reading it again. Try to crunch all those feelings together. Now, jump out of an airplane…"

Baron interrupted himself, tears in his strong, full-grown man eyes. "You know… I've been on big roller coasters, and I've since jumped out of airplanes and climbed really tall towers and I've been shot at, and I've tried drugs, and I've almost died, and now that I've experienced all those things, I realize how insufficient they are to describe it." Endorphins have nothing on the power of God.

"And now imagine that you're a kitten and you have your big lion dad standing there, and you're hiding behind his legs and nothing's going to get you. Absolute security. You feel solid, like everything is absolutely going to be okay. There is nothing to fear. Right? There's no fear. And you realize that all of this - this is why it has nothing to do with us. It's all because God is good. *He* is good. And I didn't feel any judgment for having been calloused or childish toward God. There was no condemnation at all. It was a complete reversal of what you'd expect."

After that day when he was 14, Baron would tell anybody he could about the overwhelming love of God and how it's not about our goodness. "It's all about Jesus - it's about *his* goodness and *his* righteousness, and his love for us," Baron would say.

Baron has his own story, and it's his to tell. Out of all of us, he was the most beat up by different people when he was little. He had some terrible things happen when he was a kid, and he's had his struggles as an adult.

"I'm afraid of God," Baron tells me right now. "But I'm not afraid of God because He's mean. I'm afraid of God because He's just, and I've sinned against Him so badly. If God hadn't told me He loved me, if He hadn't told me I was going to Heaven, I'd have given up a long time ago. I'd just assume I was headed for Hell. But, what I've learned is that when you focus on *not* sinning... you sin. Because the sin is your focus. We're like mirrors; we reflect whatever we're facing. If we're focused on God, that's who we'll reflect. That's why Jesus was able to sleep in the bottom of the boat during the storm; his focus was in the right place. He wasn't focused on the storm. He knew who his Father was and where his trust should be, and so he was at peace."

Baron doesn't look like an evangelist - whatever that means. He just looks like a scruffy guy trying to get through life like everybody else. He's always ready and willing to talk about God, though, and it's always fun to talk with him about God.

My brother is one of those guys that reminds us all not to judge based on appearances. In October of 2009, Baron lived in a barren apartment in Clarksville, TN. He had been out of work for some time and a soup kitchen two miles away provided the majority of his meals. In a month, Baron would get a tower climbing job, and he would have plenty of money for food. He'd fill out and build muscles that would make women stare. Even then when money was tight, Baron found his way to a nearby church to give his pitiful tithe.

Thin and hungry, Baron entered the foyer, and lovely, foolish people immediately surrounded him...

"I got saved three weeks ago," Baron told me the next time I saw him.

"What!" I asked. The evangelist got saved?

"Yeah, I went into a church to pay my tithes. I put my money in the tithes box right away, and then I got coffee. So the pastor came up, and he took me into a back room with all these elders. They asked me if I needed anything. I said I could use a ride to the soup kitchen, and they said they'd take me after church. They told me how much I needed Jesus and asked me if I wanted to give God control of my life. Well, sure, I wanted to give God control of my life."

"Seriously?" I asked my brother. "Didn't you tell...?"

Baron shrugged. "Well, they were so happy to see me get saved, and I just wanted to get my ride to the soup kitchen. And besides, I *needed* to give God control of my life. Then, the pastor gets up in front of the congregation and tells everybody that I hadn't been to church in five years, and that I had just given my life to the Lord. They were all excited. I was like, 'What? Where'd he get that? I was at church just a couple of weeks ago.'"

"Did they take you to the soup kitchen?"

"No," my brother shook his head. "No, they didn't. Yeah, and they told me that now that I was serving Jesus, my life would be so much easier. I was really put out by that. I was like, 'Really? NOW, right now my life will be easier? Where did you get that idea?'"

Baron's life has been anything but easy. Jesus didn't say it would be easy. He said, "*In the world you will have tribulation; but be of good cheer, I have overcome the world.*"[1]

We human beings make assumptions so quickly. Dr. Zenith had assumed I needed easier introductory classes because I'd been out of school a few years. Those church elders assumed that a scruffy, hungry guy needed to be saved and following Jesus would make his life easier. We freely make ignorant assumptions, and we do it all the time without even realizing it.

It is important to tell people about Jesus. People need to know he died for them. Those people at that church were good-hearted, but Baron didn't need them to tell him how to be saved; he needed food. He needed actual physical food and a ride. He needed good, healthy friends who would walk beside him so that he didn't have to go it as a lonely little flickering candle in a sea of windy darkness. What if he really had been a brand new Christian, and they'd left him to starve! Jesus wouldn't have let him starve!

People tend to jump to conclusions. We all do it. We judge each other based on appearances, with no sense of God's heart for the person next to us. We judge God based on appearances. I think if we understood the great love God has for us, we would lodge ourselves squarely between His big lion feet and stay as close to Him as we

---

1   John 16:33

could. We would trust Him. We would simply enjoy His company and curl up next to His chest. And there, we would finally hear His heartbeat.

Figure 11 - Photo by Baron Truman.

CHAPTER 9

MESSY EXISTENCE

Dr. Zenith: Class, how are we doing?
Class: (Silence.)
Dr. Zenith: Let me ask that again, out loud and in English
            instead of in my head and in Clingon like I
            apparently asked it the first time.

My personal conversation with Dr. Stillwell warmed the air that day in September, 2010. It lifted my spirits like dandelion puffs in a spring breeze.

Of course, my other relationships had to immediately smash and slide across the pavement.

Dr. Zenith had verbally smacked my hand in Dr. Stillwell's office that morning, but he yelled at me in class that afternoon. He yelled at me. Loudly.

I had been taking studious notes, but there was something I still didn't grasp, something that had failed to compute. "Why do you have to take the derivative of X to get instantaneous velocity?" I whispered to Matthew, confused.

Dr. Zenith overheard me. "Because the definition of instantaneous velocity is the derivative of X!" he hollered. "If you'd pay attention, you'd understand! Just plugging in a number for Time gives you the *average* velocity at any specific time. You have to take the derivative to get instantaneous velocity!"

"Oh! I see now," I said.

Despite appearances, I had been paying attention. I'd written down what Dr. Zenith said, but it hadn't clicked. I have often gotten into trouble in my life because I'm 86% brilliant but 11% complete moron.

Next, I made a fool of myself in Dr. Derlidger's Cell Biology, and my lab partner Maggie laughed at me in class. I'd asked some completely ignorant question because I didn't have a clue what was going on, and Maggie laughed out loud. After class she wouldn't talk to me. She wouldn't even look at me.

Pre-med Maggie had intense Filipino parents. She spoke multiple languages and played multiple musical instruments and earned straight As. She'd sit in the computer lab reading Japanese newspapers online. She hated humanity, but she did so with an entertaining gusto and we science majors had a big soft spot for her. I appreciated and enjoyed her, and I didn't particularly want her despising me. That day, she rejected me as she walked out of class.

While I sat scribbling out notes after Physics, though, the book beside me flapped shut. I glanced up expecting a disgusted astrophysicist. Instead, I saw Dr. Stillwell all tickled with himself.

"Come here," he said. "I want to show you something."

Dr. S. may have grabbed my arm…maybe he didn't… but he ushered me across the hall to his lab where he presented a rock with a few round bulges in it.

"These are cystoids," he said. "They're a soft-bodied echinoderm, and they rarely get preserved." Echinoderms are creatures like crinoids or starfish or sand dollars whose bodies have five-part radial symmetry.

"Wow," I admired the round little sea creatures. I appreciated the significance of finding soft cystoids fossilized in rock - little blobs with just a thin outer skeleton. It would be like finding quail eggs protected from the ravages of the ages!

Dr. Stillwell said, "When we go on our camping trip next week, we'll stop by a road cut where we might be able to find more of these."

Woot!

Maggie and Dr. Zenith might scorn my weak and messy existence on the planet, but Dr. Stillwell the geologist had chosen me as his pal.

CHAPTER 10

CAN OPENERS

Figure 12 - Judy Springs, West Virginia.

Dr. S: Bagels are the glue that hold it together.
AJ: It?
Dr. S: Society.

B agels are an ideal food for the hiking geology student. They
   don't squish like loaves of bread, they're fairly lightweight,
   and they are packed with carbs. When we go on camping
trips, Dr. Stillwell always buys half a store's worth of bagels. It's a
good thing that I like them.

The second week of September, we took two school vans out
to Spruce Knob, the highest point in West Virginia at 4,863 feet.

We stuffed bagels and other supplies into our packs, and we settled into a long walk through the woods down to Judy Springs. I'd selfishly filled my pack with packages of dry spaghetti, knowing I would be several pounds lighter for the seven mile hike back out.

I enjoyed the quiet march in single file through little meadows and under drooping cedars. "I get homesick for the Northwest when I hike through here," Dr. Stillwell confided to us. Half the class halted under the young oaks about two miles into our hike and waited for the lagging students to catch up. I had to hand it to the old man. The doc could still out-trek most of the twenty-somethings.

Many miles and stories later, we crossed a massive field where wild grasses swished by our waists, where nothing but green oak-coated hills bumped away to the horizon. Beyond the field, a last little rocky trail led to a spring-fed creek. Judy Springs is a quiet, wooded source of giardia and amoebic meningitis. In many places I've lived a "spring" means "clean water" - water you can drink as though it came from a water fountain. Here, "spring" meant "boil it."

I'm poking fun. Judy Springs is a lovely, quiet hideaway where elves might come out at night and dance in our camp and pipe music too high for dull human ears. A little log bridge even crosses the creek like a path to wonderland. Still… boil the water.

After we set up our tents, I crept down to the creek to check for crawdads, insectoid looking things that can be poached in boiling water and then snapped in half to eat like miniature freshwater lobsters. Dr. Stillwell and a few other students joined me on the rocks, the water gurgling near our toes. No luck. No crustaceans for dinner that night.

I turned and gazed upstream at the quaint hobbit bridge crossing the creek. "Look how beautiful that is," I murmured to my professor. "That's so gorgeous, it makes me want to cry. Certain songs do that too. The music itself."

Dr. Stillwell nodded.

I pointed across the creek to a field framed by trees. "I just want to capture it and save it. That's why I write in my journals, to not lose parts of my life."

Dr. Stillwell enjoyed the view with me. "Your journals are going to be really neat later on, especially for your kids."

"Yeah," I said. "I try to write about the kids so they can find the funny things they said and did when they were little."

"You know," Dr. Stillwell said wisely. "They're not going to want to just read the journals to find out about themselves. They'll want to read about you. Who we are isn't always how people perceive us, especially our children."

His words suggested something about himself, his own family, his own history.

That night a group of us climbed back up to the field to lie on our backs and stare at the brilliant stars. We were camped in the mountains far from any city, and that night Sagittarius dangled in the moonless black sky like a twinkly bright kettle, pouring its tea behind the southern hills. It was a time of warm camaraderie that I tucked away in my heart.

A couple of important things happened that weekend. First, I became acquainted with Dr. Jeff Gurden, aka Flash, the new young physics professor. This was our first real introduction to each other, long before I started attending his autumn bonfires. I didn't know much about this tall, quiet fellow except for the angst he caused unprepared freshmen. I discovered a thoughtful man full of curiosity, interested in everything around us and hiding an intelligent humor. While I hung out down at the creek, Dr. Gurden found himself a couple of sticks and proceeded to rub them together, Boy Scout style. He was conducting an experiment. He kept at it for a solid hour while I wandered back and started a fire the old fashioned way - with matches.

I know Flash well enough now to warn of a possible darker side to his calm demeanor. I suspect he really would hijack a Winnebago for his wife and children if war hit us and chaos loomed. He might do it just because it rained too long on a camping trip. I won't put anything past quiet, respectable Dr. Gurden. On that geology excursion, I merely enjoyed his courageous efforts to start a fire by friction. I also felt bad about beating him at cards almost as much as I enjoyed beating him at cards.

Second, Dr. Stillwell and I got into our first real argument.

We didn't *start out* arguing. A multitude of small but valuable moments filled that trip like peanuts and fudge in a sundae. Dr. Stillwell taught us about geology, of course, but many types of education presented themselves.

For instance, another girl and I learned how to tediously open cans of black beans and tomatoes for chili using the little can opener on a utility knife, because nobody had brought a respectable two-handled can opener. Slowly turn. Slowly turn. It's okay for one or two cans, but after the 10th or 12th, one's hand starts to ache. Dr. Stillwell always brings fresh vegetables, so we added real onions and peppers to our chili. Every geology trip I've joined, however, Dr. S. has failed to pack a can opener. Every single one.

"Did you pack a can opener, sir?"

"Yes."

"Are you sure?"

"Yes."

Liar!

We had fun discussions. I told Dr. S. about impaling myself on a dowel as a small child. It's a good, disgusting, bloody story. He had no interest in seeing the scar on the roof of my mouth. He told us a childhood story about half chopping off his foot with a hatchet and trudging home before quite bleeding to death. It's a good, disgusting, bloody story. He didn't offer to show me the scar.

There were serious moments too. Walking back to camp from the van one night, Dr. S. shined the flashlight on the path ahead to protect me from twisting an ankle on tree roots. "Stay on the straight and narrow," he made another of his Bible references.

Why did he do that? He seemed to hate religious people, yet he threw out little jewels like that. Purposefully.

"What is up with you?" I asked in the dark. "Did they abuse you when you were young?"

"No," he said behind me.

"Did they abuse you when you were old?"

"No," he said.

"Did they aggravate the absolute crap out of you when you were old?"

"No."

Whatever.

I didn't want a deep discussion with him anyway. I didn't know what kind of spiritual tangle I faced with Dr. Stillwell, and his personal beliefs were not between him and me. I had the impression that his issues with God were much deeper and bigger and heavier than anything I could carry. If I poked a stick into that jungle, I'd just be stirring up a mess of vipers I didn't want spilling out at me. So I didn't worry about it. I cut up peppers and onions for chili, and I made spaghetti, and I sliced cheese for bagel sandwiches. I blew on fires to get them going and I roasted marshmallows. I had a glorious time exploring the mountains and rocks of West Virginia.

Figure 13 - Seneca Rocks, West Virginia.

Sunday morning I eased out of the girls' tent before the others were awake. I strolled through the young oaks on my own, thoroughly enjoying my quiet time in the misty, sun-spattered morning. When I returned to camp, Dr. Stillwell was already rousing the late risers. "Get up! Eat some bagels! There are plenty for everybody! Have some yogurt!" he urged. "It's good to have a little culture in the morning."

We laughed unwillingly. Bagels and bad puns - the geology student's daily bread.

Despite my willingness to avoid the vipers nest, Dr. Stillwell took an opportunity that day to open up our first real conversation about religion - all by himself.

We packed up and drove out to Seneca Rocks, and I ended up at the front of the pack with both professors, climbing up the mile of switchbacks to the top of the mountain.

Something must have been chewing at the geology professor, because he suddenly started griping about the Bible. Maybe my, "What's up with you?" the night before had rumpled him.

"The Bible was written by drunk monks in the Middle Ages," he muttered.

I blinked, walking up the steep path. "What?"

"Drunk monks wrote it all down," he grumbled. "Sitting in their little cells. And people blindly follow what they wrote."

I squinted in surprise at this bit of nonsense. "Dr. Stillwell," I said, "the Dead Sea Scrolls date to the first century and earlier, and they contain the Old Testament."

"That's what they want you to believe!" he said.

"No," I said, amazed at him. I knew this stuff like he knew granites and schists. "The Masoretic Text was copied for a thousand years from the time of the Dead Sea Scrolls, and it had hardly any differences - mostly spelling changes. The Jewish copyists took the Scriptures very seriously. They didn't even correct a mistake if they thought they'd found one. If numbers in a list didn't add up right and they suspected a copyist error, they didn't correct it; they just made a note in the margins."

Dr. S. insisted alcohol was involved.

The professor wasn't actually stating his own position correctly. No scholar thinks the whole entire Bible came from Friar Tuck and a few barrels of well-fermented barley. A Jewish friend once said that he'd always believed the *New Testament* was written by a Sicilian priest, but then he started reading the book of Matthew and realized, "Wow. This is a Jewish book." It is. Jesus taught straight from the Old Testament. And of course he did.

Did Dr. Stillwell actually think "drunk monks wrote it all down" or was he just being ornery?

Flash marched behind us, saying nothing. He didn't interject his thoughts as the argument tore off up the mountain, but I could hear an occasional cough of laughter from him.

"You just believe what you've been taught," Dr. S. derided me. "You were raised in that belief system and so you followed it."

"You hung out with the communists in college," I accused the socialist beside me. "The communists are terrified of a population that believes in God, so they ridicule anybody who believes in Him. And they lie shamelessly!"

Figure 14 - Dr. Stillwell, Flash, and I enjoying the view from the top of Seneca Rocks. Photo by Karen Sutphin.

We snarled back and forth even as we hiked up the switchbacks on the tree-clad mountain. Growl, growl, grumble.

"The Right is all brainwashed," he insisted. "They sit around getting their misinformation from Fox News!"[1]

"What? You only hang out with people who think like you do. Mighty narrow-minded and old fashioned of you." I clapped him on the shoulder. "Dr. Stillwell, you need to be more progressive!"

Flash chuckled behind us.

The professors and I reached the top in record time and waited for the students behind us to catch up. There the argument ended; we had a view to enjoy.

Why did Dr. Stillwell say such foolish things? Even if he didn't recognize the Bible as the Word of God, the literature of the Bible is fantastic. Poetry and history, romance songs and angry imprecatory psalms, worship and fables - the Bible contains it all. Its variety and excellence in literature is clearly not the result of inebriated fraudsters.

Isaiah is considered a work of literary genius, one of the most brilliant volumes in all the ancient world. Luke's books are filled with medical terminology, and Luke and Acts both display an extensive vocabulary that demonstrates Luke's high level of education. The letters of Paul brim with allusions to Greek literature because he was writing to a Greek audience, and he communicated using terms they'd understand. I'd taken 23 credits of Greek and Hebrew in my previous school life. I'd studied these things. Dr. Stillwell's drunk monk theory didn't have the slightest wisp of a basis in reality. I was just getting hit with drivel from the heart of an angry lapsed-Catholic.

We ended our little battle. Dr. Stillwell had accused me of being a gullible thing that gobbled up the belief system I'd been spoon-fed as a child. I'd accused him of being sucked in by the utterly corrupt communists. At the top of the mountain our friendship danced undamaged. We didn't take any of it personally. We just watched as my fellow students climbed about on the jagged rocks.

---

1   This accusation gets repeated a lot. The situation is quite the opposite. When I was growing up, people complained about the obvious left-leaning tenor of the major news outlets. When Fox News came along, people said, "Thank you! I can watch something that's not blatantly leftist!" Anyway, I don't watch TV. A wide variety of international newspapers can be accessed for free online.

Actually, the only time Dr. Stillwell expressed real *anger* that day was after we piled back into the vans and drove off to find those cystoids.

Many miles later, we parked off the side of a highway where creamy rocks angled up into the air and exposed layers of strata - stripes of sediment that shot out of the ground at 45 degrees. Walking along the road gave us a chance to step deeper and deeper, unit by unit, into an ancient ocean bed. We were sent to examine the steep road cut for sea creatures: corals, bivalves, crinoids.

Dr. S. reserved a special spot near the vans for himself. The cystoids he sought are rare and he didn't want anybody recklessly damaging them, so he shooed off a few other students and sent them to find crinoids some yards away. He climbed up a vertical bit of rock about five feet up off the ground hunting for evidence of ancient life, and I followed him because I knew what he was after. We scrutinized the limestone rock face, peering at the ancient sea mud.

After some minutes, I eased my way down the unstable rocks, careful not to dislodge any. As the doctor watched, I muttered, "It's about evenly distributing your weight."

"No," he snapped. "It's about unbridled self-confidence."

His anger surprised me. "No, it's not," I said, confused.

"It *is* about unbridled confidence," he said. "You know it and I know it. Come on. Walk with me."

I followed him down to the van, wondering how I'd earned that little outburst. He opened the door and handed me a new cystoid specimen he'd stashed on the front seat. "Here," he said, his face hard. "I didn't want anybody trampling these. They're not easy to find."

I glanced over the petrified round sea creature, puzzled about what I had done wrong. Unbridled self-confidence? Maybe he was upset about the argument on the mountain after all.

That might have been part of it, but when I talked to him about it later, it became clear that he hadn't wanted me getting injured. I'd made him nervous, because he didn't want me to fall and break myself. It didn't appear to faze him when I told him to be more

73

progressive. Climb five silly feet up some unstable rocks, though, and he went all guard dog on me.

Dr. Stillwell and I have aggravated one another many times over the years. We've had our share of disagreements, and we've gotten genuinely furious with each other. Some things have never changed, though. We never let our differences get in the way of our friendship because deep down, we don't want the other one to get hurt.

CHAPTER 11

DRUNK MONKS

Dr. Stillwell's "drunk monks" theory of Bible authorship isn't new. His statement is completely silly from a historical standpoint, and I think it's important we clear it up a little. This is important stuff and I'd be a goober not to take one short chapter and address it. Seriously.

The Hebrew Scriptures are hugely important, and they go back many thousands of years. (See "Drunk Greeks" in the Appendix.) But, it's the New Testament that is generally credited to the well-oiled monks.

If you're really worried about it, I recommend going and hanging out with some drunk priests for a night or two. Go find some good, jovial Catholic men and fill them with wine or whiskey and ask them to write something about God. See what they come up with.

Then, sit down and read the New Testament, the whole thing from Matthew to Revelation. Compare results. It's a fair little experiment. You can even take the liberty of removing the coarse language from the priests' notes first. (Nothing but love.)

For my non-drinking friends, I can show pretty conclusively that the New Testament was not a product of the Middle Ages, and I'll try to do it quickly.

By the second century, the Gospels were already well known and we have early testimony that Matthew, Mark, Luke, and John wrote them.[1] The thing that impresses me the most, however, the thing that blisters the drunk monk nonsense, is the obvious Jewishness of Jesus. Whether or not you see Jesus as the Jewish Messiah,

---

1   See "Authorship of Gospels" in the Appendix

the New Testament writers absolutely portray him that way, and that's significant when it comes to dating the books.

It took only a few centuries for anti-Semitism to infect the early Church like a disease. It's an atrocious fact of history that the First Council of Nicaea (A.D. 325) specifically turned its back on all things Jewish, purposely instituting the date of Easter not to coincide with Passover. There were faithful Christians who wanted to celebrate the death and resurrection of Jesus Christ in connection to Passover on the Hebrew date of Nisan 14, but they found themselves fighting the Roman powers of Emperor Constantine. The early Roman Church rejected these *Quartodecimans* - "14th" guys - and excommunicated them.

In a letter to the bishops after the First Council of Nicaea, Constantine wrote:

> Let us, then, have nothing in common with the Jews, who are our adversaries. For we have received from our Saviour another way... Let us with one accord walk therein, my much-honoured brethren, studiously avoiding all contact with that evil way. They boast that without their instructions we should be unable to commemorate the festival properly. This is the highest pitch of absurdity. For how can they entertain right views on any point who, after having compassed the death of the Lord, being out of their minds, are guided not by sound reason, but by an unrestrained passion, wherever their innate madness carries them...[2]

That's anti-Semitism way past the smoldering stage. It's in full flame under the Roman emperor, and eventually there came the Inquisition and all manner of horrors. Can anyone blame the Jews for their deep resentment of historical Christianity?

But, here's my point. No priest of the Middle Ages, drunk or otherwise, would have written Jesus in Jewish terms. Yet references to his Jewishness and allusions to the Hebrew Scriptures permeate

---

2   Emperor Constantine, (A.D. 325). The Epistle of the Emperor Constantine, Concerning the Matters Transacted at the Council, Addressed to those Bishops who were Not Present. In *The Ecclesiastical History of Theodoret* (1.9).

every book of the entire New Testament. It might be hard to see if you're not familiar with the Bible, so I'll try to help you out.

Now after Jesus was born in Bethlehem of Judea in the days of Herod the king, behold, wise men from the East came to Jerusalem, saying, "Where is He who has been born King of the Jews? For we have seen His star in the East and have come to worship Him."

-Matthew 2:1-2

For verily he took not on him the nature of angels; but he took on him the seed of Abraham. Wherefore in all things it behoved him to be made like unto his brethren, that he might be a merciful and faithful high priest in things pertaining to God, to make reconciliation for the sins of the people.

-Hebrews 2:16-17[3]

King of the Jews. Seed of Abraham. Like unto his brethren. Merciful high priest. These are Jewish ideas. The Catholic Church has priests, but not the office of "high priest" that was so important in ancient Judaism.

In the Gospels, Jesus is portrayed as a Jewish rabbi who was sent to the Jews. He heals Gentiles and sticks up for outcasts like the Samaritans, but Matthew 15:21-28 makes it clear that his primary concern is the House of Israel. He teaches constantly from the books of the Hebrew Bible, and when he batters the Pharisees, he does so from within the Jewish community. The Jesus of the New Testament is a thoroughly Jewish Jesus.

I'm charmed to death by Jesus' allusion to a particular Old Testament passage.

In Numbers 21, the complaining Israelites are attacked by venomous snakes and start dying. God tells Moses to fashion a bronze serpent on a pole and hold it up, and all who look on the serpent will be healed. The serpent was nearly universally associated with evil and danger and Satan. Bronze in the tabernacle represented

---
3 KJV translation

judgment for sin. Why would God tell Moses to have them look upon a bronze snake of all things?

In 2 Kings 18:4, King Hezekiah finally destroys the brazen serpent of Moses, because the children of Israel had started to worship it. There's no other explanation for it in the Old Testament.

Then Jesus mentions that snake right before the most famous verse in the New Testament. He says:

> *And as Moses lifted up the serpent in the wilderness, even so must the Son of Man be lifted up, that whoever believes in Him should not perish but have eternal life.*
>
> - John 3:14-15

What a thing to say! Jesus associated himself with the snake that Moses lifted up in the wilderness? Isn't a snake connected with evil? Yes. Yes, because according to the New Testament, Jesus - who had not sinned - was made to be sin for us.[4] He was sacrificed in our place, taking all our judgment on himself, that all who looked on him would be healed. That's a visual aid that would make sense to the Jewish mind of Nicodemus, straight from the books of Moses.

Jesus was put to death on Passover.[5] The Jews begin their days at sundown, and Jesus ate with his disciples, telling them, "this is my body" and "this is my blood" in the evening as the Passover began. Over those 24 hours, he was arrested and tried in the early morning, whipped and mocked and finally crucified. Philip and Matthew both[6] treat Jesus as the suffering servant described in Isaiah 52:13-53:12. Each of the Gospels associates Jesus' death with Psalm 22.[7] Because he died before sunset, they did not break his legs, fulfilling Passover lamb requirements.[8]

Jesus rose again after sundown on Saturday, three days and three nights later, just as Jonah was three days and three nights in the belly

---

4   2 Corinthians 5:21
5   Mark 14:12ff
6   Acts 8:32-35, Matthew 8:17
7   Mark 15:34 and Matthew 27:46 correspond to Psalm 22:1. Matthew 27:39-43, Mark 15:29-31 and Luke 23:35-37 sound like Psalm 22:7-8. Mark 15:24; Matthew 27:35; Luke 23:34; John 19:24 all correspond to Psalm 22:18.
8   Exodus 12:46; John 19:31-36.

of the whale.[9] Jesus was raised after the "Sabbaths" (the Greek word is plural) after the Feast of Unleavened Bread, on the Sunday after Passover, on the Feast of Firstfruits.[10] These facts don't escape the Apostle Paul, once a Pharisee well-versed in the Law.

> *Therefore purge out the old leaven, that you may be a new lump, since you truly are unleavened. For indeed Christ, our Passover, was sacrificed for us:*
>
> -1 Corinthians 5:7

> *For as in Adam all die, even so in Christ all shall be made alive. But each one in his own order: Christ the firstfruits, afterward those who are Christ's at His coming.*
>
> -1Corinthians 15:22-23

These are Jewish feasts, feasts the Roman Church taught its followers to avoid. Paul, highly trained in Greek culture and Roman citizen though he was, Paul was a faithful Israelite. The early Christians saw Jesus as the heir of David, the Messiah in fulfillment of the Hebrew Scriptures.[11]

The New Testament portrays Jesus as the atoning sacrifice on Yom Kippur,[12] the manna in the wilderness,[13] the rock that Moses struck so that water came out.[14]

It's all, every bit of it, pulled straight from the Jewish Scriptures. There is no way, absolutely no way, some drunk priest in the anti-Semitic Middle Ages would have come up with any of that.

---

9   Jonah 1:17; Matthew 12:40.
10 Leviticus 23:11; Matthew 28:1. I think Jesus was crucified on Wednesday just before the "Sabbath" of the high feast of Unleavened Bread. Leviticus 23:5-8; John 19:31.
11 Luke 1:32, Acts 2:36, Romans 1:3.
12 Leviticus 16:14-16; Number 19:1-12; Hebrews 9:11-15
13 Exodus 16:15,35; Numbers 11:7-9; John 6:30-58
14 Exodus 17:6; 1Corinthians 10:4.

CHAPTER 12

MANHATTAN

When Dr. Stillwell and I were climbing up the mountain, neither of us were just giving each other lines from a political ad campaign; we were speaking from our hearts. I think our comments to each other really nailed some basic attitudes we both had.

THE COMMUNISTS

When I gave Dr. Stillwell my criticism of the communists, I wasn't spouting capitalist propaganda. I said it to him because when I was 11-years-old, I found my mother's FBI identification card in a box I was unpacking. "What's this?" I showed it to her. "Oh. Don't worry about that," she told me. It turned out that Mom had been an FBI informant on the Communist Party in Los Angeles, California during the Vietnam era. Remember, this was the same woman who jumped out of airplanes and broke apples in half with her bare hands. Same woman. She was a young and beautiful Vietnam widow, and the FBI approached her and asked her to join the Communist Party on behalf of the American people. For three years she traveled with top communist leaders in America, helping organize anti-war marches and attending high-level meetings. My comments to Dr. Stillwell were based on the contents of those meetings.

Los Angeles is not a small, inconsequential town, and my FBI-connected mother was in the very heart of some political machinery that's still chugging today. She explained that the communists wanted to implement policies and ideas that destroyed the American nuclear family. That sounds outrageous, but the whole point was to weaken America, so they could control the American people. They also hated the fact that Americans believed in God. For their goals to be accomplished, there could be no higher power than the state - and they needed to get God out of the American mind. It was all about control, and not only was deception acceptable to them, it was encouraged and taught. To this day, Mom will be listening to some political leader speak, and she will say, "There. There it is. Did you hear that? That was a line they were teaching us to use 50 years ago."

I am confident that most people who enter the socialists' camp just want the world to be a better, more fair place. I believe that's the group Dr. Stillwell is in. However, the agenda of communist/socialist leadership has constantly proved itself to be Machiavellian in its methods, the epitome of ends-justify-the-means immorality. They always preach all the things we want - social equality, justice, peace - but they never ever produce those things. They just take control, commandeer everybody's money, and use tyrannical methods to force each person into submission. The U.S.S.R., North Korea, China, and Cuba are all good examples of the utopias produced by Communism. Europe is rotting inside out from socialism, and Germany's industry and hard work won't be able to hold up the rest of the Continent forever.

We can see it on the small scale too. The famous cult leader Jim Jones was an ardent communist/socialist. I know his is an extreme case, but his Jonestown reminds me of every communist government out there. Jones gathered followers with cries for justice and social equality, throwing out Christian-sounding phrases to look respectable, but ultimately calling religion "the opiate to the people," quoting Karl Marx.[1] The FBI recorded Jones' meetings both before and after he moved his people to Guyana, and his whole goal was a Marxist utopia. The man was an atheist with a God complex. He was not even pretending anymore when he said:

> I have tried to reduce myself as a person, but there's no way that you can reduce the center and circumference of the universe. I am

---

1   Jones, J. (n.d.) Transcript Q 1053-4, Prepared by Fielding M. McGehee III. Alternative Considerations of Jonestown and Peoples Temple. Jonestown Project: San Diego State University.

the only fully socialist. I am the only fully God. So I'm now on the scene. I'm going to project myself, I'm going to push myself, I'm going to declare myself... I have commanded you to feed the hungry, I have commanded to give water to the thirsty, I have commanded you to let the captives go free, I have commanded you to fight against capitalism from the beginning of time, and now I say, put your blinders on and go forward.[2]

That makes my eyes widen. Holy smokes that's crazy! Jones promised his followers a paradise in the jungles of Guyana, and they trooped down there with him, but he also required absolute obedience and loyalty. Anybody who caused trouble faced serious punishments, including beatings and time in "the box." His speeches mixed truth and lies to manipulate his people, and they make me queasy to read. In 1978, Jones led more than 900 people to drink poisoned punch, including 287 children. He murdered them all.

My bottom line is that I don't trust anything that comes out of the mouth of leaders who champion Karl Marx. The communists always claim to be fighting inequality, but they never produce peace between people groups. Instead, they produce constant class warfare. They call themselves "socialists" and cry for social justice, but they consistently produce poverty and death. There's a remarkably consistent track record there.

I want the world to be a good place for everybody too. I don't want old people left to die alone and poor. I'm against racism and sexism and greed and cruelty. But, because I want the world to be a better place, I'm going to oppose the socialists forever. Thank you.

THE BELIEVERS

On the other hand, there have been plenty of shameless leaders who have used religion to subjugate people. The communists don't have the monopoly on controlling the masses through tyranny. Dr. Stillwell had accused me of being gullible - just following the religion I'd been taught as a child. How could I prove that he was

---

2   Jones, J. (n.d.) Transcript Q 1053-1, Jonestown Project.

incorrect? What did I have in my arsenal to demonstrate to people outside myself that the God I believe in is real and that I'm not just following the social construct I was given as a kid?

The subject came up at lunch with Dr. Derlidger not many months later.

"Is there any situation that could prove to you that God doesn't exist?" the Lidge asked me calmly over his salad one day. Biology professor Dr. Derlidger, "the Lidge" had settled across from me in the lunch room. People sat around us at other tables, chatting and munching. He and I chatted and munched as well, and soon we entered a friendly discussion about God and faith. Somehow those discussions started naturally between the Lidge and me, whether I wanted them to or not.

The Lidge did not get heated during these kinds of talks; he didn't seem to have the anger and bitterness that boiled up in Dr. Stillwell. Even in that moment, the Lidge remained the gentle science professor. His wore his collared shirt with the top two buttons undone and his thick white beard trimmed short. He made deep discussions a relaxing pastime, because we could just talk honestly and openly without being emotional.

His question was a good one. What set of evidence might prove to me that God didn't exist? He meant, was my faith in God falsifiable? Could it be disproved by any massive wall of evidence against it? It was a reasonable thing to ask, because that's what scientists do. We set up hypotheses that can be tested, and the best way to test a hypothesis is to try and disprove it. It's when we *can't* disprove something that we establish some confidence in it.

However, I didn't know how to answer Dr. Derlidger in that moment. It would be like asking a guy from New Jersey if there were any scenario that would disprove the existence of Manhattan.

God is still doing things in the lives of ordinary people. I run into them all the time. These people are not fanatics or emotionally weak nut jobs. They include the guy who does the design work for local bulletin boards or the carpenter who finishes people's basements. The people we see every day on the bus have had encounters with

God and His power and love. Their lives aren't perfect or pain free, but God has let them know He's there.

Now, it's likely that Dr. Derlidger does not hear the same stories that I get to hear on a regular basis. Why? Because he's an atheist biologist. Polar molecules attract other polar molecules. Nonpolar molecules attract other nonpolar molecules. I just don't think that Dr. Derlidger hangs out with the same people I do. I am hungry for God, so I attract other people who are hungry for God. I willingly tell people the things that God is doing in my life, and that gives them the freedom to open up to me.

Of course, it's still *me* they're talking to. So, when a man like Tony Darmanin tells me a cool story about having his torn guts healed instantly, I tend to cold-call his mother to get more information.

I've been to Manhattan many times. I can verify that it exists. I also know God exists. I live in His Spirit. I've seen His power over and over again, and I've learned I can depend on Him. Still, I wanted to be able to answer Dr. Derlidger's question. Is there some way we could reasonably falsify God's existence?

MAKING PREDICTIONS

Doing science is all about making predictions. That's what hypotheses are. If we can make a prediction, we can test it. For instance, in an attempt to falsify God's existence, we might work to show that there's no difference between believers and nonbelievers. For instance:

Hypothesis: There will be no significant difference between the number of major miracles experienced by believers and unbelievers.

This is called a null hypothesis. We can test it to see if it can be rejected with a high level of confidence.

Let's say we go for it. We set up the experiment with exquisite care. We narrowly define what qualifies as a "major miracle." We also narrowly define who qualifies as a "believer" or "unbeliever" for the purposes of our experiment. We interview a huge group of random people from all manner of backgrounds to test our hypothesis, and we remarkably end up with 9,500 "believers" and 9,500 "unbelievers."

In one scenario, we compare their number of major miracles, and we find that "believers" experienced 171 major miracles while "unbelievers" experienced 174 major miracles. Woah. We didn't expect that. We run some statistical tests, and it turns out we can't reject the null hypothesis after all. There is no significant difference between the two groups as far as miracles are concerned. Only 1.82% of our test subjects experienced a major miracle, and miracles were experienced by both groups equally.

This scenario certainly doesn't provide a strong argument for belief, does it? But does it disprove God's existence? Honestly, the answer is "no" for some boring statistical reasons. This experiment simply indicates that believers and unbelievers are equally as likely (or unlikely) to experience major miracles. On one hand, it certainly suggests that being a believer isn't worth the trouble. (On the other hand, there are still 345 major miracles to be explained.)

Let's consider another scenario. Let's say there were 1895 major miracles between both groups, and 1786 of the miracles were experienced by believers. In this scenario, nearly 10% of our test subjects had experienced a major miracle. There is a significant difference between the two groups, and most of the miracles were experienced by believers. We are pleased! We can reject the null hypothesis! But does this prove God's existence? Honestly, the answer is "no," for some boring statistical reasons. It simply means that believers have a much higher probability of experiencing major miracles. (Even then, there are 1895 miracles that need to be explained.)

We could run a variety of experiments like this, but they all have some serious difficulties by their very nature. The unbelievers might have believers secretly praying for them, and we'd never know it. What's more, miracles are difficult to verify, especially since hospitals are not free to talk about their patients. It's good to collect witnesses, but it would be better to have access to actual medical records.

We also cannot say why most people *didn't* experience miracles. I think every major miracle requires an explanation, regardless of whether we can explain non-miracles, but those of us who still suffer in pain would like to know what gives. "Hi, Lord. Not chopped chicken liver here. Hello?"

When it comes down to it, we have a serious problem as cool, objective scientists: we cannot predict what God will do. He could exist and never do anything we expect. That just means God doesn't subject Himself to scientific inquiry and has nothing to do with whether He's real or not. Dr. Derlidger asked me if the existence of God was falsifiable, and I don't think it is.

Besides. God is always picking the most unlikely characters. I'm convinced that God loves each one of us, but He often uses the *last* person we'd expect in order to reveal Himself.

> *But God has chosen the foolish things of the world to put to shame the wise, and God has chosen the weak things of the world to put to shame the things which are mighty; and the base things of the world and the things which are despised God has chosen, and the things which are not, to bring to nothing the things that are, that no flesh should glory in His presence.*
>
> 1 Corinthians 1:27-29

I've often thought that a Down's syndrome child might do far more to make this world beautiful than some of the richest geniuses out there. We often find that it's the kid with cerebral palsy who teaches the people around him to be gentle and to love one another. I think of the dying thief on the cross who became a source of hope for millions. He had no clue that the entire world would hear about his last words with Jesus,[3] or that multitudes would depend on those words for their own salvation. God chooses the most unlikely people.

Even if God Himself is not falsifiable, we can find His fingerprints all over the place. He still does things. He's not Carl Sagan's invisible dragon in the garage. We are surrounded by a great crowd of witnesses

---

3   Luke 23:39-43

who have met Him. So, what do I say to Dr. Derlidger?

A PREDICTION THAT MATTERS

There are a couple of ways to demonstrate that Manhattan is, in fact, an empirical reality. The best, of course, is to go there.

I think the same thing is true about God. We can depend on other people's stories, or we can find Him ourselves.

Of course, anybody can get on a train or plane or boat and get to New York. It doesn't seem as simple to touch the invisible God of the Universe. Yet, I'll wager there are 50 times more people who have encountered the Spirit of God than have ever been to New York City. Not everybody has the money or

Figure 15 - My youngest, Zekie, on the Ellis Island ferry in 2012. One World Trade Center is under construction behind him.

means to get to New York, but God can touch people wherever they are. He's there for the asking, no matter how poor we are.

At the same time, those who have the resources to zoom off to New York might be the very same ones who struggle to find Him.

Last week as I write this, I was talking to John Contreras and Paul Barrett, a couple of tattooed Harley enthusiasts, along with Harry Lenhard, a three-decade professional geologist for U.S. Silver. All three men are committed Christians, and John is now a pastor. John told me something I'd heard many times from different sources:

"We go into other countries - Dominican Republic, Mexico - and people come up for prayer and we see them healed right and left - boom boom boom."

"What kinds of things? What have you seen people healed from?" I asked him.

"Name it," John said. "Name it. Blind people regained their sight. People with some really nasty diseases healed. Deaf people able to hear. All the things you read about in the Bible. But then you come back to America and…" he trailed off.

I've heard this same experience repeated from various people - big, whopping miracles take place in impoverished nations and among oppressed peoples.

Why? Does God hate rich people? Not at all. Abraham was wealthy, and he was called the friend of God.[4] However, God notably resists the proud and gives grace to the humble.[5] When people have no other choice than to trust Him, that's when He seems to come through. That's when He comes through in my life. Jeremiah 29:13 tells us that those who seek God have to seek Him with their whole hearts, and how many of us actually do that? Even most poor people in America have new shoes and smart phones. We eat every day. How many of us are determined to find God and know Him?

We also have better access to medical science in America than in many other locations. Science and medical knowledge are blessings that have saved countless lives, and God gave us brains for a reason. We should take advantage of our clean water and sterile surgical equipment and brilliant surgeons. But, we have to be careful. So often in the West, we've told God, "We don't need You anymore."

Science can't run tests on God, but individuals can still hunt Him down. Maybe that's the hypothesis we can make, the one each of us can test on our own:

Hypothesis: Those who seek the true God with all their hearts and don't give up will find Him.

While the prophet Jeremiah wept over the inevitable destruction of Jerusalem, he told its inhabitants:

Let not the wise man glory in his wisdom, Let not the mighty man glory in his might, Nor let the rich man glory in his riches; But let him who glories glory in this, That he

---

4   2 Chronicles 20:7; Isaiah 41:8; James 2:23
5   James 4:6; 1 Peter 5:5-6

understands and knows Me, That I am the LORD, exercising lovingkindness, judgment, and righteousness in the earth. For in these I delight," says the LORD.

Jeremiah 9:23-24

Does my belief in God affect my work as a scientist? Yes, but not in the way people usually assume. The God I serve is all about what is true, so it's my job to seek out the truth as honestly and diligently as I can.

Even now, when I doubt who God is, I say to Him, "Whoever you are, You, the God Who Does Exist, I want to know You. You are the one I serve. Help me to know You better."

I think that's safe. That works.

CHAPTER 13

ALWAYS THE STRAWS

Michelle: Dr. S. doesn't want me to graduate. He wants me to stay here ten years.

Dr. S: Then you'd be tenured.

Michelle: That's... That's not even funny. I'm smiling only because it's so bad.

I was on time to Dr. Stillwell's 8:10 class every day before our Seneca Rocks camping trip. Every day. I had been late to Dr. Stillwell's class several times the spring semester, and I was pleased with my excellent record during the fall. Being late is such a shameful thing, but it's one of my big weaknesses. From our little cabin, it was an hour's one-way trip to school on busy, congested roads. If traffic held me up or if I had to wait 15 minutes to get the children into their school or if I got stuck behind a school bus...

Living in our van while the cabin got gutted actually helped me get to school on time.

A 50-year-old handyman named Gary had spent the summer tearing out our rotting bathroom and replacing everything, including the subflooring. When we'd returned from our summer adventures, my

Figure 16 - My newly finished bathroom floor. Dr. Stillwell kindly cut the tile that snugs up against the toilet.

bathroom looked awesome, but a patch of swollen and flaking particle board floor still puffed up where my kitchen counter used to sit. Boxes and extra furniture thoroughly blockaded my living room.

Over the course of the fall, I populated our house with everything Gary needed, and I did it all within my small rehab budget. A lady in Alexandria listed her entire five-year-old kitchen for $700 because she wanted to replace it all with stainless steel appliances. Gary and I loaded the matching Frigidaire refrigerator, gas stove, microwave, dishwasher and maple cupboards into my van and got them all home in one single haul.

A family in Potomac, Maryland planned to tear down an aged house and build a new one, and I was able to pull up hundreds of square feet of solid wood oak floors for $200 before the people destroyed the old place. I picked up a free steel front door from a fellow in Bethesda and new Anderson windows for $50 each from farmers in Pennsylvania.

The mismatched ceramic tiles for my bathroom and kitchen I'd snapped up that spring at a closeout for $5 total. Gary marked the tile edges that needed to be cut, and Dr. Stillwell let me use his rock saw to do the job. Yay rock saw!

In the meanwhile, the kids and I lived in our conversion van with its cozy bed and propane stove. We stayed in this house-on-wheels while our long-neglected cabin developed into a pleasant little home.

I actually liked living in the van. I could park down in town at night. In the morning I could wake up the little ones, help them get dressed, brush their hair, make up their lunches and give them some breakfast. I could drive around the corner to their school door and head out to my own school. It made it so easy to walk into Dr. Stillwell's geology lab before class started at 8:10. I was doing really well until late September.

A week after we returned from the camping trip, I slipped into the geology lab one single minute after class started. It was so stupid, because I'd managed to get to school early. I'd even popped by Dr. Stillwell's office and dumped off some chocolate miniatures for the benefit of other visitors, so he knew I was on campus somewhere (fighting the printer in the computer lab). The problem with arriving to his class even a minute late is that I sat on the *other* side of the *front* of the room from the door. No being subtle.

Still, the day glowed warm and sunny. I felt on top of the mountain; my life was a big fat old sunflower and I was enjoying its seeds sprinkled over the chocolate ice cream of friendship and acceptance. That particular day, Dr. Stillwell taught us how to use compasses correctly. Nobody had ever taught me how to use a compass the way they're supposed to be used. Never ever. I loved it.

Then, Dr. S. took our class out on a geology walk. It was one of those wonderful days in September when the air was fresh and gentle, and oaks in their full greenery towered overhead. Our school sat in a charming historic burg with wooden doors on the main street that opened into book stores or toy stores or bike repair shops. We strolled down the sidewalk past the doors of brick houses, hands in our pockets.

Poor Michelle Caerphilly wasn't with us. She had gotten ill on our camping trip.

"You heard that Michelle is sick?" I asked Dr. Stillwell as we walked along.

"Yes, she called me," he said.

"Do you know what she has?" shaggy Whitaker ambled beside us.

"She caught a case of meningitis on the trip. That's why I tell you guys to boil the water before you drink any of it," Dr. S. said.

"Poor Michelle," I said. "I know she's miserable. I enjoy her a lot."

Dr. Stillwell nodded, "So do I."

"Although, she does get annoyed at me when I'm disrespectful to you," I smiled.

"Yes," Dr. Stillwell agreed. "She also gets annoyed when you're late to class."

I had been looking at the cracks in the sidewalk as we walked. At that, my head popped up. I mean, Michelle hadn't even been there that morning.

"But, I was doing really well for a long time!" I protested.

"Like when!" Whitaker scoffed.

"The whole first month of school!" I said.

And Whitaker and Dr. S. proceeded to tease me.

It was such a small thing, but that slight rebuke from the doctor overwhelmed me. In those ten seconds my radiant sunflower got stomped on and its little happy seeds scattered and crushed all over the ground. I could handle being yelled at by Dr. Zenith and ignored by Maggie. I didn't like it, but I could bear it. But these two men whom I admired and respected, whose warmth I valued, these two men gave that light scolding and a surge of shame swamped over me. It was physical and oppressive and it swallowed me up.

I felt like a bottle of carbonated effort. I had been trying so hard, so hard, and I'd been able to hold it all together without spilling more than a few drops here and there. I'd been able to contain the stress and grief and a multitude of tasks, little and big. I'd been able to deal with my failures and find time to cram in studies and write news articles at night for money and work on my house and care for the children and all their needs. The first anniversary of Randy's death had just passed, and even its pain hadn't killed me. That morning I'd been feeling good about myself, happy that I was doing okay! I was managing it; life was lovely and sunny and fun!

That one small shake of my bottle, that little teasing upset, and the full year of doing it on my own finally burst suffocating misery inside me. I felt instantly smothered by my aloneness, overwhelmed by the difficulty of carrying so many heavy burdens in one solitary little soul.

I couldn't bear it. I had to walk away from them.

The crowd of students made its way down tree-lined Mill Street toward the park on the edge of the Potomac River. Large rocks poked up in the park thirty feet high. Dr. Stillwell gave us a short lesson on the geological concepts of strike and dip, and we were sent to climb all over the rocks to practice measuring rock bed direction and angle.

I tried to get my emotions together, to calm down. I tried to figure out the strike of the rock and use my compass to determine its orientation, to practice my new life skill.

I turned to Dr. Stillwell. "Um, how do you know which face of the rock to use to do strike?" I looked up at the multi-sided mini-mountain before me. There seemed to be rock faces looking in every direction.

The doctor didn't answer my question. He just shook his head and groaned, "Oh, the inflexibility of chemistry majors."

Inflexibility! I couldn't believe he'd just said that to me. I thought, "I'm the most ridiculously overly-flexible person on the planet! I'd be on time every single day if I weren't so painfully flexible!" I glared at him, enraged at his adding another punch to my already bubbling mess. I just needed him to answer the question!

"You don't know me," I snarled.

His eyes widened. "…Oh-*kay*."

I pushed my way past him. "Would you get out my way? … Please."

That made it even worse, letting my frustration erupt onto the good doctor. I could not believe I had just said, "You don't know me." In my family, we made fun of people who said that! We would joke, "You don't know who I am inside! You never have! I'm going to run away and never come back *ever*!"[1] And *I* had just said something so silly, and I'd been hostile to a man who treated me like I mattered!

Dr. S. led the students up the steps of the town monument while I remained down below. I couldn't follow them. I couldn't breathe. I turned my back on them and held my hands over my face and let warm tears blub down my cheeks.

The Potomac River didn't notice, meandering down there at the bottom of the hill. The low rock wall didn't notice, separating the park from the steep, tree-tangled slope. I didn't want the people up on the steps to notice. I just felt like a mountain had dumped on me.

I wiped my face and rubbed the back of my hands across my eyes and took a breath. I didn't want a set of flaming red eyes and a glowing nose in front of a whole class of students. I took a few more breaths and turned to follow everybody up the steps. I looked

---

1   Ahem. Thank you to Steve Oedekerk's *Thumb Wars* for this parody of whiny Luke Skywalker.

up, relieved to see that most were facing the monument. Except for Dr. Stillwell, who had reached the top and stood watching me.

The professor turned back to the class and gave an educational spiel, then everybody poured back down the steps. We had to walk down the road, and I tried to keep to myself and behave like a not-horrible human being.

Ten minutes later we dropped back into our seats, and fellow student Billy asked me questions about the upcoming minerals test. I had managed to breathe like a normal person by then. "Make your own chart and put all the info down for each mineral," I suggested. "And write it out by hand - it will help you remember."

Billy showed no sign that he knew I'd just been snotting on myself. Billy didn't sense how utterly embarrassed I felt. I survived the rest of the class time, keeping my eyes down for most of it. I didn't dare meet anybody's gaze.

After class I waited for the others to leave, then I followed Dr. Stillwell out.

"I'm sorry," I faced him in the quiet hallway.

Dr. Stillwell shrugged it off. Then, with emotion, he said, "I just want you to be *okay*."

That was probably the best thing he could have said to me. The heartfelt concern in that one sentence soothed away my shame.

"I got hit with some straws," I said.

"It's always the straws," he agreed.

"I don't want you to feel sorry for me," I said to him.

He nodded. "I don't."

I needed his understanding. I needed him to forgive me. I said that last bit, though, because I honestly didn't believe I had a right to his pity. I had filled my plate to the top with responsibilities, but my life was good. My children were healthy, and I was able to feed them every day and surround them with loving people. I lived in a time and place where I was free to take geology classes without fear that Boko Haram extremists might break into the school and force me into sexual slavery. I didn't have to worry that any paper bag on the street might contain an IED ready to detonate. I'd gone on dinosaur digs, and I'd watched lightning ripple along the underbelly of clouds. My life was full of adventure and excitement, and one day I was going to leave and spend eternity with a Father who loved me.

Nobody should ever feel sorry for me. My life is pretty darn fantastic. Still, I appreciated Dr. Stillwell's genuine interest in my welfare. We all need the freedom to have a meltdown once in awhile, and we need the people around us to have compassion on us when we do.

CHAPTER 14

THE PATERFAMILIAS

"As a civil engineer, my greatest hope is to never appear in the news. If I end up in the news, it means I need a lawyer."
- Matthew Caerphilly

One of the beautiful things about that week, one of the reasons I saw the sunflower in life, was that Matthew's mother had invited me and the kids to stay at their farm just outside of town. Living in the van was convenient, and I liked it. But, we had actually spent the previous night eating dinner at a dining room table. It was a wonderful thing.

And the best thing was that Matthew's dad wasn't there!

It turned out that Michelle Caerphilly's big friendly husband was Matthew's older brother, and Michelle had not enjoyed her experiences with her in-laws. When her husband Nathan was falsely accused of stealing from his work, Michelle's in-laws offered Nathan bail money with big strings attached.

Michelle told Dr. Stillwell before class, "My parents would have said, 'Oh! You're in trouble? We'll give you the money and help you out.' Not them, though! Nathan's parents said they would *lend* us the money, and we have to follow a repayment plan."

As Michelle related her frustration, Dr. Stillwell busily set up paperwork for class and didn't look up to respond.

From Michelle's perspective, the Caerphilly parents were unloving, legalistic sorts of people. So, when Matthew invited me to study physics at his parents' house, I felt like a bit of beef jerky venturing into a man cave.

I had to study physics, though. I absolutely had to do well in that class. Matthew and I hunkered over our textbooks at his dining room table, reading every paragraph out loud and discussing the implications of Newton's Laws. I holed myself up on the kids' top bunk at the cabin on the weekends and penciled out problem after problem while the children ran around outside.

It paid off. When Dr. Zenith returned our corrected first exams, only two people in the class had earned an A. Yep, Matthew and the chupacabra! Haha! In fact, I would have beaten Matthew by one point (Bam! Bam! Bam!) had Dr. Zenith not docked me two points for shortcutting on the final problem. I had the correct answer, but I'd run out of time and didn't have more than a few seconds to scrawl out all the work. So, I'd drawn an arrow to my work from earlier in the problem and written, "The same as this."

"Actually, he's right," Dr. Stillwell said when I complained.

"Symmetry arguments do not prove anything," Dr. Zenith responded. "And I could take off additional points if you want to push the issue."

"No, that's fine," I smiled. "I'll show all my work in the future."

I'd visited the Caerphilly farmhouse a couple of times before I even met Matthew's parents, and when I first spoke to his mother, it was while her husband was out of town. Suzanne turned out to be darn okay, a friendly woman with a wonderful laugh. In fact, after that first physics test, Suzanne asked me, "You're living in your van with your children? Do you... do you want to stay *here* for awhile?"

Well, sure! Matthew's dad and sisters were on vacation at their cottage in Massachusetts, and Matthew and his mom had the house to themselves. For one glorious week, the children and I slept on the futon in the Caerphilly music room and enjoyed Suzanne Caerphilly's homemade food. For a week I milked the goats with Suzanne in the evenings. How fun is that! Milking goats!

Suzanne and I became close, fast friends. She had been raised just north of Seattle, and we both had attention deficit issues. We understood each other. We bonded easily.

It took another week or two before I finally met the rest of the family, including the *paterfamilias*, Dr. Toby Caerphilly. Toby was not from Seattle. No, Toby had been raised in Massachusetts. What does that mean? It means that he was not from Seattle.

One evening in early October, Matthew's father walked in the front door, and I heard Suzanne greet him in the other room. I felt no eagerness to deal with Dr. Toby, the harsh lord of the manor. I had been grateful for his absence, thank you. Now I had to resign myself to the end of my tranquil time at the Caerphilly home.

"Amy Joy!" Matthew shouted from the kitchen. "You need to come meet my dad!"

I got up to follow my friend out of the dining room. "He's a family psychologist," Matthew told me cheerily as I wandered into the kitchen. "Hey Dad, this is Amy Joy!"

"A family psychologist?" I said in surprise. Why hadn't Matthew said that before? My animosity weakened. I had been thinking about getting the kids some counseling, because I didn't want them turning into monsters five years after their father died over unresolved emotional issues. Sammy had panic attacks if he didn't know exactly where I was every minute. He lived in constant fear that I would die. Zekie hugged the legs of strange men who came to the door, and when we flew out to Seattle, he wanted to jump out of the airplane midair so he could see Daddy in Heaven. He started crying because I wouldn't let him jump out of the airplane! Savvy concerned me most of all because she didn't express herself. She internalized her emotions, but I knew they would pop out in some form, and I wanted her to know how to deal with them.

My children needed help, and here appeared a family psychologist. Maybe Dr. Caerphilly possessed redeeming qualities.

As I had this revelation, there stood the man himself in his white dress shirt and tie, freshly home from work. Matthew grabbed my arm and dragged me across the kitchen to the silvering head of the Caerphilly family.

I met the man's serious gray eyes. "You're a psychologist? A family psychologist?" I repeated what Matthew said, just to make sure. My kids needed some professional guidance and I knew it. "I know I shouldn't even ask you," I started, "but would you... would you mind talking to my children a little? Would you be okay with that? They lost their dad last year, and I want to make sure they're working through things okay."

From his father's point of view, Dr. Caerphilly knew his 20-year-old son had been spending a lot of time around this widow with three children, and he wanted to assess the situation. Who was this young lady staying on his futon for a week while he was gone?

Dr. Caerphilly loosened his tie and unbuttoned his top button.

"They lost their father?" he responded from the doorway, just inside the farmhouse kitchen. He undid the buttons on his cuffs. "You mean, you didn't lose your husband?"

"Well, yes," I stood before him. "But, I'm concerned about them. I'm not concerned about me."

Dr. Caerphilly had finished adjusting his attire and his gray eyes studied me. "Why are you distancing yourself from your husband?"

He kept asking the wrong questions!

"I'm not distancing myself from my husband," I said. "I'm just not interested in talking about me."

"Why don't you want to talk about you?"

Frustration agitated inside me. That's not what I meant at all. "No. It's not that I don't want to talk about me. I just... it's irrelevant. I'm interested in making sure my kids are okay. I'll be all right. I need somebody to talk to my kids. Last week Savannah finally cried about her daddy's death in her first grade classroom. It's been a year, and she's never cried for him."

It had taken her a year to start verbalizing her grief after her cat was killed by a car. She doesn't process grief quickly.

"She cried in her first grade classroom, but she didn't cry with you?" Dr. Caerphilly said. "Why do you think she hasn't cried with you?"

Dr. Caerphilly. That man. That man interrogated me. He interrogated me! What kind of warm and helpful family psychologist was this, anyway! He poked and prodded and asked me a wide variety of questions, and he did not do so gently, by the way.

After my interrogator finally let me go, Matthew accompanied me outside into the farmyard.

"I've never seen him talk to anybody that way before," Matthew said, embarrassed. "He's very good. He's a great psychologist. He knows people, and he would never have talked to you that way if he didn't think you could handle it."

I thought he was unnecessarily annoying.

I've dealt with far worse than Dr. Toby Caerphilly, and I continued to meet with Matthew to study physics while my kids ran around outside with the chickens and goats. I continued to visit Dr. Caerphilly's home and eat his cereal and occasionally sleep on the futon in his music room. I continued to visit the Caerphilly home, even though I sometimes had to breathe air in the same room as the *paterfamilias*.

In ancient Roman law, the paterfamilias had authority over everybody in his household, including extended family members, adopted family members, freedmen or slaves, and eventually Toby decided that I belonged in one of those categories. The situation turned out better than I anticipated, of course, because Dr. Toby Caerphilly isn't a monster. Not even a little.

I later thought about Dr. Stillwell's reaction when Michelle complained about Nathan's bail money. The geology professor hadn't said a word; he just let Michelle talk. Dr. Stillwell had taught Nathan in his class, and when I brought up the matter of the bail money months later, Dr. Stillwell said to me, "They did that because they *knew* Nathan."

God bless Nathan. I like him a lot. He's friendly and easy to talk to, and he freely admitted to me that his grades in Dr. Stillwell's class had been less than stellar.

Michelle misjudged her in-laws, and she didn't really recognize what Nathan's parents did for him. Dr. Caerphilly found a good lawyer for Nathan and together with Michelle's parents fronted the retainer money (which Nathan was never able to pay back). Dr. Caerphilly accompanied his son to court to support him during a really stressful time. The lawyer got the case dismissed and Nathan never had to go to trial. Michelle just needed more perspective.

And me? Toby just knew that the most important thing for my children was that their mother was okay, so that's where he started.

Eventually, the children and I were invited to stay at the Caerphilly house on Tuesday nights - my news deadline night - a tradition we continued for two years. Eventually, I'd stop in and make dinner on a Sunday afternoon and give Suzanne a break. Eventually Zekie would help with chores by sweeping the stairs or collecting eggs. Savannah would go watch while the girls milked the goats, and she had the privilege of witnessing the birth of a set of twin kids the next February. Sam climbed all over the Caerphilly children's playhouse and played on the Wii. When Matthew built another barn behind the farmhouse, he and his father made sure the railings on the stairs would be Zekie-safe.

First impressions can be utterly incorrect. Dr. Caerphilly often came home late Tuesday nights to find me writing articles on his living room couch while my children slept on his futon. He's actually a full-fledged clinical psychologist who diagnoses every manner of mental illness, and he regularly testifies in court about criminals' mental health. He deals with people and their problems all day long, yet he would still stop to ask me about my day and the weekly events of my life.

He didn't interrogate me after that first meeting. He would sit in his armchair by the wood stove and let me unload whatever was on my heart. We had informal evening counseling sessions every week or so for two years, and I've gotten to where I can talk to him about anything.

Toby did take time with my children and would occasionally encourage me that they were doing well. He played games with them and laughed with them and told them stories before bed. He hired me to help Matthew build that new barn, and he changed the locks on my cabin when people kept kicking in the door. He invited us to spend the 4ᵗʰ of July with his family at their beach cottage in Massachusetts, and he'd hand me gas money when I had none. Two weeks ago as I write this, he called me up and offered to lend me some money if I needed help for a down payment on a car. Toby and Suzanne Caerphilly welcomed me and my fatherless little kids into their home and into their lives.

"You're the most difficult of my children," Toby told me at the youth fair one summer.

"What!" I protested. "I do the dishes!"

I cannot begin to describe the blessing the Caerphillys have been to me.

Dear Michelle. I wish Michelle had been able to enjoy her father-in-law without getting turned off by poor introductions. They didn't know each other, that's all. Toby Caerphilly is not legalistic or harsh. Oh, he sometimes gets on my case about little things, but if there's ever anything we need, the Caerphillys are willing to help figure something out.

And if you want some excellent goat milk feta or camembert or chevre, they sell cheeses at local farmer's markets every weekend.

Figure 17 - Emily Caerphilly and a new baby.

CHAPTER 15

THE BEATING WITH COOKIES

I had earned an A on our first physics test, but Dr. Zenith still did not give me a break. No. He'd give us problems to do in class, and he'd walk around behind us and double check what we were doing. If I did something wrong, he'd correct me. If I worked out the problem just fine, he wouldn't say a thing.

After he'd yelled at me on September 1st, though, I decided I would sacrifice myself and stop writing down his hilarities in my journal. I closed my notebook, and I set it aside. I folded my hands and gazed steadily at him while he spoke. After that, Dr. Zenith calmed down and seemed to relax a little toward me.

Then, there came a day when Dr. Zenith didn't criticize me for anything.

"I won!" I told Matthew. "I did it! Ha! Now the game is to see if I can get him to compliment me for something."

"You can never win," Matthew said, "because as soon as you do, you change the game."

That was part of the fun of it.

I dropped my pencil on the ground a few days later, but rather than barking at me to pick it up, Dr. Zenith actually picked up the pencil *for* me and tossed it to me. And I caught it.

"Good catch," he said. "You have redeemed yourself."

Ha! A compliment! I win again!

Still, Dr. Zenith might never have said a truly pleasant thing to me, had it not been for the day Matthew and I both found ourselves locked outside of his door.

Lab reports for Dr. Zenith's class were due every Thursday at the beginning of class. We had one week to write up the lab report for the previous week's experiment, and that was it. On this particular Thursday, Matthew and I had been struggling to get the answers we needed for the report due that day.

I wanted to try and run a few more experiments, so I hunted down Dr. Zenith that morning and asked, "Hey, Dr. Zenith. Can I use the equipment in your lab? I'd like more numbers for our report."

Rather stiff and calloused, he said, "No. If I do it for you, I have to do it for everybody."

I have never appreciated that argument. I've always felt there's a certain stingy self-imprisonment that comes from demanding that everyone's apple juice glass be filled to the same level. People who insist that the world should be fair are doomed to lifelong frustration. Most importantly, nobody else was clamoring to Dr. Zenith to let them into his lab, so it was all nonsense anyway. All he had to tell me was, "No." That's it. It was his lab and he owed me no explanation.

I returned upstairs after he rejected my request. Matthew and I continued laboring on the problem for our lab reports, and we were not getting numbers that made sense. It wasn't working. We struggled and fussed for hours, rewriting and refiguring over and over again. We weren't doing it right!

Finally I said, "Matthew. He won't care. We just have to get to class and turn these in."

"But it's not right!" he said.

"It doesn't matter!" I said. "If we don't go now, he won't accept them at all!"

"But I can figure it out. I know I can," Matthew insisted.

"So *what* - he won't accept your report!" I said. "I'm going to class." I finished typing up my last paragraph and glanced up at the clock as I printed out my paper. I was five minutes late. I grabbed my backpack and ran down to Dr. Zenith's lab.

I reached the large double doors and shoved down on the long steel handle. Clunk. Of course, it was locked. I sucked in a long, deep breath, and I knocked.

A few seconds later, the door swung outward and Dr. Zenith stood above me. He glared at me straight on with his irises pointing in opposite directions. It created an interesting white-eyed effect in his dark-skinned face, and it could have been intimidating in a horror flick. He pointed up at the clock on the wall above his PowerPoint station.

"Do you see what time it is?" he asked.

"Yes, sir," I said.

"Why have you come late to my class?"

I let out a deep breath, defeated. "Because, I've been working on that problem all day long, and I still haven't been able to figure it out," I said.

He paused a moment and then moved slightly to the side. "Come in," he relented.

I dropped my backpack by my seat and grabbed the stapler, preparing to place my report in the pile.

"Amy Joy," Dr. Zenith warned from behind me, "I don't know that I'm going to accept that."

I didn't argue with him. He'd let me into the room, which meant I'd be allowed to do the work for that day. If he'd turned me away at the door, I'd have received zeroes for both weeks' lab reports.

Our third lab partner, the ever-sharply dressed Mike Smith (complete with collared shirt and tie), started setting up the acceleration experiment for the day. I asked Mike how he'd solved the problem that Matthew and I had struggled over. He'd made a trendline. Of course! That's how we should have done it! We were young and inexperienced!

About an hour into the lab class, there came a knock at the door. Mike's eyes widened. "Dear God," he said. "Who is that?"

I didn't turn to look. I just closed my eyes and shook my head. "It's Matthew."

Dr. Zenith didn't even stand in the doorway; he strode into the hallway with Matthew and shut the door behind him. I didn't expect bloodshed - it was Chia Pet genius, after all. Still. Dr. Zenith is a no-exceptions kind of guy.

A few minutes later, Matthew came bouncing in and joined Mike at our experiment.

Matthew objects when I tell this story. "I did not bounce," he'll say. "I was feeling mortified."

Yes he did. He bounced.

Dr. Zenith didn't let it go, though. Not even a little. Toward the end of class, Dr. Zenith came by and said, "I want to talk to you two after class." At the very end of class, as we cleaned up the materials from our experiment, he said, "I want to see you in my office in three minutes." Oh my goodness. I felt like we were in the fourth grade on our way to see the the headmaster.

"Wow. I'm not sure I want your names on my lab report," Mike joked at us.

(Maybe he wasn't joking.)

Matthew and I finished putting our tools back in the cupboards. With one minute to go, we grabbed our backpacks and headed out the door and down the hall. As we walked, we argued about the problem we'd failed to figure out.

"You have to do a trendline like Mike did," I said. "You have to. That's the way to do it."

"But we can do it mathematically!" Matthew insisted. "I know we can!"

As we argued back and forth, I kept thinking, "What in the world am I going to say to Dr. Zenith? What can I say that will soothe that impossible man?" I couldn't think of anything in those few moments before we reached his office door.

There was nothing drab and dull about Dr. Zenith's office. The walls rained down degrees and accomplishments and magazine articles that featured his face, but the room fit a man who joked about street justice rather than the stern astrophysicist. A half-sized R2-D2 model guarded his floor. A big framed poster of the Starship Enterprise filled one side of his north wall and comics tattooed his desk. A spinning gyro-like object whirred on his filing cabinet and Star Wars breakfast cereals lined his (covered-over) window sill along with a wooden dragon and action figures and a black and white picture of Dr. House's head and a stuffed Spiderman with bling around his neck and... Describing Dr. Zenith's office is like trying to capture the multitude of flashy things in the cockpit of the Millennium Falcon.

We reached the open door of his office and stood before his desk. Yes. He sat behind his desk and we stood before him. He the ruler, the monarch, and we the condemned subjects. I didn't know what secret vaults with chains and henchmen lay beneath his Spiderman welcome mat; we couldn't put anything past Dr. Zenith. That's why the words from his mouth shocked me.

Dr. Zenith gazed at us for a moment. Then with no preliminaries, he shook his head and said, "You guys. You cannot cannot CANNOT allow one problem to so *consume* you that it causes you to drop the other responsibilities in your day. It was just one problem. Just one. You might have lost a few points if you couldn't finish it, but that's okay. You don't have to get every answer right all the time. It's okay to let it go and focus on other priorities."

I stared at him, unable to accept what I'd just heard. Had he just dismissed the paradigm of perfection that he'd previously fired like bricks into my brain? The man was actually suggesting we give up on something that he had assigned - that his problems were not the only priority in our lives! Not a greater priority than coming to his class, anyway.

"I'm not sure how I'm going to handle this," he said. "You weren't late because your alarm failed on you or because you were out partying last night. You were late because you were *doing physics*, and you had a problem you couldn't solve and you *couldn't let it go.*"

Delight burst like a rainbow of jelly beans into my soul. That's right, Dr. Zenith! Preach it!

"I don't have to tell you what scores you two got on the first test. You know what scores you got. I don't have to tell you. You're some of my best students. You're actively engaged in class and you're asking questions and clearly interested in the material. I'll bet you did every problem in the chapter," he said to Matthew.

"I did all the odd ones," I muttered. The solutions to the odd problems were found in the back of the book, so we could check the answers as we learned to work out the problems correctly.

"I'm not sure what I'm going to do," Dr. Zenith frowned deeply. "I have to think about this."

I realized that our professor had actually encountered a serious conundrum. Dr. No-Exceptions never accepted reports from students who came late to class. He didn't allow students to hand in late assignments. I realized he was speaking out loud to verbalize an internal brawl over how to deal with this singularity.

"Do I accept your reports? What if you become like my friend Tom in college, who always turned assignments in late - and they always let him get away with it? Will you be like Tom? Or is this an aberration, something that won't happen again?"

"It's an aberration," we both said. At least in his class, (let's be honest).

Dr. Zenith talked on and on and on, puzzling and stewing. "The only reason you are standing here right now is because of your previous excellence. If you had shown less diligence, I wouldn't have even let you in the door this afternoon. I believe in grace, but I'm not sure I need to show you additional grace beyond what I've already shown you."

He took a breath, and we thought he was wrapping up. Then he started up again and continued for several more minutes.

"I cannot say whether I'll accept your reports," he finally said. "I'll think about it. Even if I do accept them," he said, "I won't give you full points."

We both nodded. "No. That's fine," we said.

"Okay," he gazed soberly across the desk. "I'll let you know what I decide next week."

We left the Zenith office and walked calmly down the hall, past Flash's office door and Dr. Stillwell's office door and outside into the courtyard. As soon as we stood beneath the bright blue sky, we discharged laughter from gleeful hearts. Dr. Zenith had allowed words of approval to pass over his lips into the open air. Mostly about

Matthew, but he'd let me be included. I had broken through the constant nitpicking and criticism, and I had received almost-praise!

"He beat us, and he gave us cookies!" Matthew declared.

Ever after, we have referred to that encounter as the Beating with Cookies. My troubles with Dr. Zenith were not over, but that day offered the first real positive sentiment I'd ever received from the astrophysicist, and I will treasure it always.

CHAPTER 16

LEX

I was four-years old, and it must have been wintertime, because the hydrangea bushes poked up brown and barren one story below me. I hung by my ankles, staring down at the multitude of twigs. That summer the bushes would hold vast blue blossoms and fat bumblebees would hover merrily about their business, bzzz zum bzzz. At that moment, the yard below loomed cold and bleak. It was a long way down.

I wasn't frightened. If I had let terror take over, I would have started struggling, and if I had struggled, Lex might have accidentally lost his grip. Even at four-years-old, I knew it was smartest just to hang calmly. I knew that Lex would hang on tight. Even though his stupid teenage friends were laughing, my brother wouldn't drop me. Not on purpose.

Mom came around the corner of the house just then and saw me dangling out the second story window.

"LEX!" she barked. "You pull your little sister in right this minute! What are you thinking? She could fall and break her neck!"

He hauled me in, but Mom's yelling continued.

Half a year later, Lex and I walked down a shaded forest path on a summer afternoon. As I trotted along beside him, Lex spied an enormous hornet's nest hanging just a few feet into the bushes. I can't remember whether the hive was attached to a fir or a maple, whether the tree was large or small. I just remember the massive hornet's nest bigger than my head hanging there off the path.

"We should knock down that nest," Lex said. "Amy, as soon as I tell you to, you run. Run as fast as you can."

115

"Okay," I said.

Lex took up a thick branch stump. "Ready, set...." it took him an agonizingly long time to finally knock down the hive. I don't know why I bothered waiting; you'd think one of us would have had some sense. As soon as he said, "Go!" though, I sped down the path with my little legs a whir of energy beneath me. Cedars and huckleberry bushes blurred by. I could run endlessly in those days, and I raced out from under the wooded canopy and across the street into our house perfectly safe. Lex, though. Lex's forehead was spotted by a mess of stings, and Mom had to ointment him all over.

I adored my big brother. I planned to marry him when I grew up, because I loved him so much. No 14-year-old boy wants his five-year-old sister hanging around him all the time, but I wanted to follow Lex wherever he went. If he hiked through the woods and across the little airstrip, I wanted to go too. If he played 45s on the record player in his room, I wanted to sit on his carpet and listen with him. It didn't matter if we were playing Monopoly or rocking out to Pat Benatar, I loved spending time with my big brother.

"You wet the bed!" he complained when I wanted to climb into bed with him when I was little.

"No I don't!" I insisted. I didn't mean to wet the bed.

"Mom! She can't sleep with me. She wets the bed!"

He got mad if I messed with his records or cassette tapes. He didn't want me following him everywhere. He was a teenager, and I was a small child. He wanted to hang out with his idiot teenage friends.

"Your real parents are swamp things," Lex told me. "They live right down the road, and one day they're going to come to get you and take you back to the swamp with them."

"Mom! Are my real parents swamp things?"

"No, honey," Mom said.

I didn't know how to take it the time he told me I was adopted. My friend Carla was adopted. The possibility existed.

"Am I adopted?" I asked my mother. It was an issue, especially with that whole swamp-creature thing lingering in my mind.

Mom responded by giving me my first lesson on evidence and logic. "Honey, you have my blonde hair and my blue eyes and my freckles. Don't you look just like me, hon? That's how you can know you're not adopted."

Wow. Good point.

I leaned back on Lex's bed one day while he swung a watch back and forth in front of my eyes. "You're getting very sleepy," he chanted. He ordered me to close my eyes. "Now, when I click my fingers, you will open your eyes and you will not remember what you did when you were hypnotized."

Snap. My eyes opened.

"I hypnotized you!" he said. "It was so cool!"

"No, you didn't," I said.

"Yes, I did! We went to McDonalds and ate cheeseburgers."

"No we didn't. We didn't go," I said.

"Yes we did! You don't remember because I hypnotized you!"

"No, you didn't."

I learned at an early age to not believe most of the things Lex told me.

Late in the October of my third grade year, Lex came to get me from my classroom. By then, four more small brothers and sisters had joined our family, but only little Heather and I were old enough to be in school. Lex had come to get us both only halfway through the school day.

I started the questions as soon as we stepped out of my classroom. "Why are you picking us up early Lex? Huh? Lex, why are you picking us up early?" I bugged him all the way down the hall.

"Shhh," he said, "Wait until we get outside."

"Why are you picking us up early, Lex? Why? Why are you picking us up early?"

"Shh!"

"Why Lex? What's going on? Why are you here?"

He relented and told me. "Mom's been in a car accident. We're going to go see her in the hospital."

"No she hasn't," I didn't believe him. "Why did you really pick us up, Lex? Why?"

"Yes, Amy, she was in an accident."

"No she wasn't."

When we reached Lex's truck, though, I saw all the balloons and flowers, and I knew my brother wouldn't go through all that trouble for a joke. Tears instantly spilled down my face.

A picture of our smashed Ford Pinto made the front page of the *Eastside Journal* in Bellevue, Washington. Three-year-old Baron had nearly hemorrhaged to death, and he spent two weeks in the children's hospital before they released him. Mom had broken her femur and crushed her wrist. She lost the baby she'd carried for eight months, our unborn sister Hope.

Maids took over the house while Mom healed those first few months, when she couldn't walk to chase after toddlers. Over the years, little slivers of glass would continue to work their way out of her scarred forehead. That car accident affected us for a long time.

Lex was gone most of the time by then. He had a job. He had friends.

Even though he teased me sometimes, I knew that Lex loved me. He gave me rides in the wheelbarrow on top of leaves and grass clippings when we had to do work in the yard. Sometimes he let me tag along with him to the 7-11 so I could buy penny candy. Every Christmas he'd jostle me awake at 7:00 am, when it was safe to start making noise.

"Hey Amy! Santa came. Get up!"

A few months after my ninth Christmas, Lex left to San Diego to make his fortune. He did it, too. He made his fortune. He worked his way up in the fashion world, and twelve years later I went to visit him in Columbus, Ohio, where he told all the buyers what to buy for Victoria's Secret.

"You…uh… you need any bras?" Lex asked me one day during my visit.

"Sure," I said.

So, Lex took me bra shopping, because he knew more about Victoria's Secret merchandise than the sales lady did. I'll tell you, it's great fun to go bra shopping with your big brother. He breezed around the store picking out undergarments and tossing them into the changing room for me to try on.

"Where's the second skin satin?" he wandered off to find that section.

Mom often says that Lex is the most truly generous person she knows. I opened the pantry door at his condo and saw one bit of evidence; at least ten boxes of Girl Scout cookies loomed from the shelf overhead - cookies Lex would probably never get around to eating, just because some poor kid showed up on his doorstep to sell the things.

That week in Columbus was the first time I'd seen Lex in eight years. He picked me up from the Greyhound bus station and we drove out to eat some dinner. While we zoomed along in the car, somebody pulled sharply in front of us and Lex had to hit the brakes. Instinctively, he reached over and put his arm in front of me to keep me from smacking into the dash. I had a seatbelt on, and I was a 21-year-old adult, but my big brother still reached over to protect me.

Lex now lives in New York and serves in the top echelons of a major clothing retailer. When the kids and I visited him recently, he took us out to the m&m's and Hershey's stores at Times Square. Sam said to him, "I can't decide whether to get this T-shirt or this chocolate." Lex said, "What? Get them both! Get whatever you want!" Cool Uncle Lex.

Having Lex as a big brother affected me at a fundamental level. I never assumed that people would want me around, because I was used to Lex's, "No, you can't go with me." I considered rejection normal, and I didn't feel crushed when kids my age ignored me. I know Lex didn't mean to make me feel rejected. It's just what happens when you're the little sister of a teenage brother.

At the same time, I loved Lex and I wanted to spend time with him. I missed him. He was my hero, and his absence left a huge, overwhelming hole in my heart. It has never gone away. He didn't die, but it's almost as if he did because I so rarely get to see him.

He attended my wedding. He called me when Randy died. We've been keeping up by email and texts, and he writes me back. I have an open invitation to stop by any time I'm in New York. Yet, here I am years later, grieving because I miss my big brother. It's plain difficult for us to get together, and we don't get to see each other more than once every year or so. Still, it's always great to have Lex around.

It doesn't take a psychological genius to figure out that the absence of Lex from my life has affected me and my adult relationships. When I turned 16 and men started seeing me as a woman, it annoyed me. They didn't understand. I didn't want romance; I wanted my brother back.

I still like having big brother types around. I'm good at treating people like they're family. I'm ready to be skeptical of certain things people tell me, but I'm also good at forgiving people who hang me out windows.

CHAPTER 17

THE LIDGE

I stared at the question Maggie had scribbled into my Chemistry fraternity pledge notebook. "What's the name of Dr. Derlidger's wife?"

I wanted to join Sigma Pi Epsilon - those wild and crazy chemistry students - and I had to fill out a hodgepodge of odd questions from existing members as part of the process. The questions varied from, "What's the difference between a cofactor and a coenzyme?" to "What's the difference between an orange?"

Maggie wanted me to learn the name of Dr. Derlidger's wife?

Dr. Derlidger's Cell Biology class beckoned me after Physics every other day. I struggled at first because I'd ordered the wrong textbook from eBay. But studying the biology of the cell? Exploring the intricate world of life taking place behind the phospholipid bilayer walls of every tiny room in our bodies? That's fantastic stuff right there!

The Lidge taught us about these miniature cities in the cell, cities complete with garbage collectors and architects, factory workers and contractors and policemen and security guards. The microscopic characters of Cell World have to be able to communicate with each other. Gone are the days when we thought the cell was just a blob of goo.

Let's say a protein floats through the cellular fluid, and it needs to get inside the nucleus to make itself available for use in chromatin. It can't just waltz into the nucleus. No. It has to get through the gate, where the bald guy with the flat knuckles checks IDs. It has to pass through a nuclear pore into the guts of the nucleus, and it needs a

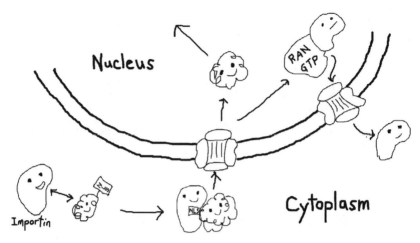

Figure 18 - Importin transporting a protein with an NLS into the nucleus.

limousine and a gold card to do it. The limo is a nuclear transport receptor called "importin." Get it? Importin is important because it imports proteins. The gold card is a nuclear localization signal (NLS), a specific sequence of amino acids that acts like a shipping label. When importin pulls up next to the protein and sees the NLS on it, it buckles that baby in and acts like a personal driver, transporting the protein into the nucleus. Hooray, the protein makes it through the pore. Inside the nucleus, a chunky Ran-GTP grabs the importin, saying, "What you doin' in here?" The protein hops off inside the nucleus, where it is free to go about its business. Meanwhile, the Ran-GTP yanks the importin back into the cytosol, giving it the boot. There the importin hangs out, waiting for another bit of protein that needs a ride. Proteins that don't have the right NLS might get picked up by a passing garbage truck called a lysosome, which will eat defective particles and destroy them in acid. Yes! Self-contained garbage disposal trucks!

The Lidge taught these marvels, using much larger words and fewer story pictures.

Proteins need special gold cards to enter different organelles too, like the endoplasmic reticulum (ER) and the mitochondria. Mitochondria produce the majority of the cell's energy (they are often called the powerhouses of the cell). Each mitochondrion has

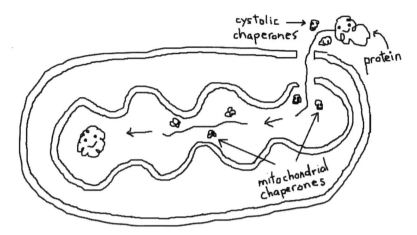

Figure 19 - Chaperone proteins feeding a protein through a mitochondrial wall and helping it refold on the inside.

two membranes protecting it, an inner layer and an outer layer, like two sets of free-floating skin. In order for proteins to enter a mitochondrion, passages in both the inner and outer membranes have to line up with each other. The protein has to have the correct signal on the front - the correct address label. Then, the two membranes of the mitochondrion have to line up to make a passage. After the membranes line up, proteins still can't just squeeze through the corridor, because proteins naturally fold up in bulgy, tangled-looking shapes. To handle the job, chaperone proteins both inside and outside of the mitochondrion take charge of the process. Like good chaperones, they tell the proteins to "straighten up" and then feed them through the narrow hallway between the membranes. On the inside, mitochondrial chaperones help the proteins refold again so they can go off to do their protein jobs.

The passages have to line up! The protein has to be straightened and fed through by chaperones! Holy smokes!

A whole city of communication goes on inside the cell. The extent of cellular interaction can intimidate any biochemistry student, not to mention the casual observer of a metabolic pathways chart.

The cell is amazingly intricate. In fact, the Lidge would go out of his way now and then to tell us, "This evolved. It wasn't designed." He went out of his way to say that. Of course he did, because when a person gets in there and considers all that cooperation and detailed messaging necessary for every single cell to function - and then for all those individual cells to work together as an organ - and all the various organs to hum together as a system in the body as a whole - the first thing anybody thinks is, "Dang!"

At lunch months later, I told the Lidge, "But that's your opinion. You don't know whether it was designed or not," and he nodded in agreement. I mean, it's true. He was just expressing his viewpoint. Dr. Derlidger is a smart guy with a high-octane vocabulary; I like him a ton and after this conversation I'm about to tell you, he and I became friends. In fact, I recently baked his zucchini casserole recipe and posted a photo of it for his wife on Facebook. At the same time, he's a self-described Humanist, and the first fundamental dogma of Humanism is that the universe is self-existing and not created. There might be a whole bunch of folks in scientific circles who agree with his materialistic interpretation of the data, but I needed more than a, "Because I said so," from him.

There at the beginning of my time in Cell Biology, I had no interest in arguing with the Lidge. He was entitled to his personal views, and the other students were all adults free to make up their own minds. I felt no responsibility for what Dr. Derlidger decided to believe about how the cell got to be the marvel we've grown to know and love.

Then in mid-October, Maggie made it necessary for me to ask the Lidge about his wife.

After class, I approached the 60-something man with his trim white beard and glasses. Dr. Derlidger filled out his button-up shirt like a good cook should, but he still played racquetball and rode his bike long distances. Sturdy. The Lidge is sturdy.

"Hey Dr. Derlidger," I said. "I'm trying to get into Sigma Pi Epsilon, and I need to invade your personal life and find out your wife's name."

We stood at the front of the room in one of the school's larger lecture halls. He glanced up at the distant ceiling and said, "I haven't seen her in so long. I can't even remember."

I felt the distress flood my face. "Ohhh... You need to hang out with your wife! You need to make dates with her!"

He smiled. "We do have dates, but we've both been so busy lately. She plays the flute, you know. So, she's been gone playing in Martinsburg, and she's been busy doing work for the church."

That startled me.

"Really? What church do you go to?" I asked him.

"I don't go," he said. "She goes to the Methodist church in town." He paused, and then he divulged his secret. "And her name is Becky."

Wonder of wonders. Humanist Dr. Derlidger's wife Becky faithfully volunteered at the Methodist church.

Interesting.

"I'm not religious, but I support her in it," he said. "I consider it a placebo effect, but I figure that if it helps people to believe in something then that's fine."

I studied him for a moment. Then I told him, "When I was a baby, my herniated belly button was healed, and my grandmother called my mother from two counties away to tell her, 'Check Amy's belly button. I think God healed her.' There has to be a mechanism for that. As a baby, I wouldn't have been affected by the placebo effect."

I had consciously made the decision *not* to care about worldview wars with the Lidge. Yet, that little interchange started a conversation, and we started walking out of the classroom. We walked together across the patio outside, and we walked up the hill all the way to German Street, where we enjoyed dessert at a free ice cream social in front of the big clock tower. On the way, we talked about Richard Dawkins and Bertrand Russell, God and miracles and sex. Thanks to Maggie's little question, Dr. Derlidger and I had a warm and friendly philosophical discussion across the whole campus, and we ended with a little bit better understanding of the other. It was the first real discussion we'd ever had, and it opened up our eventual talks over lunch in later months.

The Lidge told me, "There's a book I think you'd enjoy called *Finding Darwin's God*. I had a copy, but I lent it out. If I get it back, I'll be glad to lend it to you."

"Okay," I told him. "Sure. I'll be glad to read it."[1]

The Lidge demonstrated no fluster at all when I explained that God showed me things and did miracles in my life. He assumed there were alternate explanations that I hadn't yet considered.

"I've experienced miracles in my life too," Dr. Derlidger said. "But we do not take the easy way out and cheat and just use God as an explanation. We don't find answers that way."

I understood that. "But, I'm not a materialist," I told the Lidge. "I'm not going to limit myself and look at the world as though only this physical world exists, because I don't know that."

The reason we don't want to cheat and use God as an explanation in science is because we want to find out the actual cause of things, and we don't want to give up prematurely. If God *is* the real explanation at the bottom of things, then nothing else is going to fit. The Humanists won't allow God to be a consideration at all ever, and that's a bit foolish if God reigns after all. We shouldn't decide in advance - based on personal philosophy - what we're going to *allow* as the answer to our questions. We should collect as much information as we can and try to follow where that information leads.

"You know what gets me?" I said as we walked up the hill past the library. "Sexual reproduction."

Gonads! Gonads are amazing. I am absolutely serious. Even sea urchins have them. In fact, that's pretty much all you find inside a sea urchin - just a five-fold set of gonads. And if you eat sea urchins, well... that's what you're chewing. Yet, sea urchin gonads produce fully functional eggs and sperm.

Where did gonads come from? Especially (especially) since single-celled algae like the *Dunaliella salina* in the Great Salt Lake fuse together just like eggs and sperm - but without any gonads to produce them. They reproduce by isogamy, in which the algae gametes are all the same size. But even then, the *D. salina*

---

1   I eventually bought my own copy. See "Why the Book *Finding Darwin's God* Irritates Me" in the Appendix.

have mating types. The "-" mating type will only fuse with the "+" mating type, just as eggs will only fuse with sperm. Other algae reproduce by oogamy, which involves a large, stationary egg and a small moving sperm - just like we have. But, oogamy in animals and oogamy in algae came about independently,[2] and these eggs and sperm don't have gonads producing them.

That's completely mind blowing. Which came first, the eggs or the ovaries?

David Kirk at Washington University in St. Louis readily acknowledges the historical struggle of biologists to understand the evolution of sex. There are a lot of mysteries, like why sexual reproduction exists at all when asexual reproduction works just fine. We can see reasons why sexual reproduction is *useful*; mixing up the genes from two parents offers more genetic variability in the kids. This means greater flexibility among the offspring to survive in different environmental conditions. That's great.

However, why bother with splitting up into males and females? Wouldn't it make more sense to have just one sex? Dividing animals into males and females cuts the number of potential mates in half, making it that much harder to find an appropriate sexual partner. (And when it comes to women and men trying to co-exist, good grief! It's amazing our species has survived at all). Yet, Kirk begins an article on oogamy by stating, "The male-female dichotomy has evolved independently in nearly all lineages of multicellular organisms."[3]

That's just crazy. There are males and females throughout the plant and animal kingdoms. If I were predicting evolutionary development from single-celled organisms, I would have never predicted a male-female dichotomy. Never. I don't think "boy" and "girl" would have evolved even once, let alone over and over again. Sexual reproduction doesn't require more than one sex type. It doesn't require male and female. It just requires two haploid gametes fusing to make a diploid cell. So, why males and females? Why not just one

---

2   The many groups in which oogamy has evolved independently include animals, fungi, red algae, brown algae and several different kinds of green algae." Kirk, D. (2006). Oogamy: Inventing the Sexes. *Current Biology*, 16(24), R1028-R1030.
3   *Ibid.*

sex that produces haploid gametes? Partners could still selectively choose the best mates, and they could do so without having half the population cut off from them. Yet, throughout the plant and animal kingdoms, we find sexual reproduction that requires males and females to reproduce, both sexes made just right to puzzle-piece together. There is no sexual reproduction that isn't accomplished by female and male parents, or at least by (+) and (-) mating types. I am fascinated.

According to the Bible, God created male and female at the very beginning. He set it up that way. Genesis 1:27 says, "*So God created man in His own image; in the image of God He created him; male and female He created them.*" If we're making predictions based on worldviews, the creationist viewpoint predicts and explains the ubiquitous existence of male-female sexual reproduction. Evolutionary biologists can develop reasons why sexual reproduction makes sense, but not why it can be found everywhere. Even hermaphrodite plants produce both male and female gametes. I don't know a single situation of sexual reproduction that involves parents of only one sex.

I didn't get into all of that with the Lidge. I just asked, "How did the egg and the sperm both evolve in the first place, ready to fit together perfectly to provide two sets of chromosomes for each new creature throughout the history of evolution?"

"Hmm," the Lidge said. "I've never thought about that before."

Even as he responded, I knew my professor wasn't changing his mind about anything. That wasn't my purpose in talking with him. The purpose was the open exchange of ideas, both of us free to speak our minds and say what we thought.

We reached the ice cream social and ate our ice cream, then we parted.

That whole moment amused me. I hadn't had any intention of discussing things with Dr. Derlidger, and yet the discussion took place anyway.

Why did Dr. Derlidger feel obliged to tell his students the cell wasn't designed? The cell, with all its interdependent parts, its whole city of busy little characters - we *have* to believe that natural processes developed that little marvel on their own or we're bad scientists? Really? Why! "We can't use God as an explanation" does not justify the naturalistic viewpoint, but that's what it always seems to get back to. According to the professors, the cell *must* have evolved by natural processes because that's the only choice biologists are allowed.

I have a really hard time with this issue. As a scientist, what's the difference between assuming that every part of our bodies has a purpose because it was engineered - and assuming that every part has a purpose because natural selection favored it? I personally think that the best explanation is a combination of the two; the engineering came first, and part of that engineering involved flexibility that allowed different phenotypes to succeed in diverse environmental conditions. That makes real sense to me.

I actually think that the grand theory of Evolution is treated like a deity these days. I mean it. No matter what we see, we see it because of course Evolution in one of its various moods would have worked that way. It's called on for everything, no matter what it is, and so often there's no difference in saying, "Evolution did it," and "God did it." Nothing but the name of the deity.

CHAPTER 18

THE WHIFF

"If you can hold it in the palm of your hand without screaming, then you know it's cool enough to pour."
- The Lidge (on making agar)

I enjoyed discussing things with Dr. Derlidger that lovely October day, but I didn't have any interest in trying to get him to change his mind. That would have been ridiculous. The man had a doctorate in biology. He had worked in biological research for years. I didn't. I hadn't. It was his business what he decided to think about the world, and I just didn't worry about it. I didn't want that responsibility.

On the face of it, I was a rotten Christian. Really. I should have been concerned about Dr. Derlidger's position in eternity. If God created the universe and the life in it, then the Lidge was in huge trouble. Here was a man who insisted that the brilliance of the cell magically put itself together, a supreme insult to the Engineer who taught chaperone proteins how to straighten their younger brothers and slide them through the portals of mitochondria. And not only did he reject his Maker, the Lidge taught other people to do the same. He's the sort you'd expect God would want to flick in the head and knock past Mars.

I didn't burden myself with the state of Dr. Derlidger's soul. I had decided not to worry about his eternal salvation or his worldview. I'm only one little person, and I can't carry the weight of the world. We had our discussion on the way to the ice cream social, and that was it. I didn't ask for that conversation, and I didn't seek another.

Then, two weeks later, God showed me how he felt about Burt Derlidger, antagonist to the Faith.

It was an exceptionally normal day. I sat on a stool and tried to pay attention to his instructions as the Lidge demonstrated how to run a gel to separate proteins. Normally I would have been at the table with my lab partners Maggie, Sarah and Allie, smack next to the demonstration table. For some reason, I sat in the middle of the room two tables back.

I had been wanting to pray and was having a hard time. It was one of those days where it didn't matter what I wanted to pray, it wasn't the right thing. There was a disconnect between my brain and what was going on spiritually, and I didn't know how to get the two lined up (like mitochondrial membranes)! For me, prayer is often like giving a massage. I have to feel around until I find the spiritual knots, if that makes sense. I had to work around to discern what matter actually needed prayer. That day, I couldn't find the knots, so it was hard to pray. I sat there in our Cell Biology lab classroom, struggling in myself while watching the Lidge talk about separating proteins. As I sat there, a surprising thing happened. I was suddenly hit with a whiff of how God felt about the Lidge.

It was a whiff, like the kind you get when pancakes are frying downstairs. The odor floats up the stairway strong enough to wake you up in the morning, but you know you're catching only a little taste of it. You know that if you walk down into the kitchen, the warm aroma will billow into your face much heavier, more thick and substantial, than that tiny, wispy breath you managed to inhale from your bed. As I sat there watching Dr. Derlidger set up a gel electrophoresis, I caught that little whiff, that waking-up whiff of God's heart toward the Lidge.

Half a year later, I told Dr. Bob Manchester about the whiff over a table at lunch. Dr. Bob leaned forward. "What was it?" he asked with some excitement. So I told him, and he seemed disappointed. But, he shouldn't have been disappointed, because how God feels about Dr. Derlidger *is* exciting.

"But, isn't that what you already believe?" Dr. Derlidger said when I told him - shortly before Dr. Manchester sat down. "You believe God loves us."

"I know," I said, "But I wasn't worried about you. Sorry, I'm a bad Christian. And besides that, there's a huge difference between believing something in your head and knowing it in your knower - really living it in the reality of your life."

So, I sat there in his lab watching the Lidge ready gels for the experiment, and this whiff hit me. I felt it all through my chest, and it was not a whiff of overwhelming love. That wasn't it. It was a *longing*. The emotion of it was a lung-squeezing longing, the way a father feels about an estranged son he doesn't get to see. He just wants the boy with him, but the son is clear across the country and never calls or writes or comes home. It's a terrible feeling. What I sensed was exquisitely intense and pained, but I knew I'd only caught a faint breath of it. The full heart of it had to be much broader and deeper than I could imagine.

"Ohhh… Wow. I forgot," I said to myself sitting there on my lab stool. "I forgot that's how He feels about us."

When the prophets told us that God is longsuffering, they really meant He is *long suffering*. Yes, He's huge. Yes, He's holy. He's powerful and brilliant and terrifying. He is. And yes, He allows us to break His heart for a long long time.

Dr. Derlidger stood at his lab table pipetting proteins into gel columns.

"Okay, Lord," I said. "If You love him and You want him, then I'll pray for him."

So, I started praying for the Lidge that day. Not because I had to make him think the same way I did and not because I needed him to be part of my little faith group. I started praying for the Lidge because I love my Father in Heaven, and I wanted Him to have His son come home.

CHAPTER 19

WINNING THE WAR

The week before Halloween, I stood in the hall outside Dr. Stillwell's office door, staring out the windows and enjoying the radiant heat and the bright outside world. The hallway door opened and Dr. Stillwell and Dr. Zenith both walked through.

"Don't jump!" Dr. Stillwell said.

"It's not worth it!" said Dr. Zenith.

I was super entertained, because their hallway is on the first floor and the window was not even open. I smiled and pulled out a waiver I needed Dr. S. to sign.

"You know," I told Dr. Stillwell. "Every time I'm in here, Dr. Zenith comes along." I looked at my watch. "I make bets about how long it will take him to show up."

"Well, *you* are in here a lot," Dr. Zenith countered.

"I am!" I said. "But I always have a legitimate reason. Or I find one."

Dr. Stillwell signed the paper and handed it back to me.

"Maybe… maybe coming in here is just part of your shhhedule," I said, British style.

"Shhhedule?" the non-twin doctors both repeated.

"That's how Dr. Manchester says it," I said.

"You should be careful," Dr. Zenith warned. "They lost the war."

The Revolutionary War. I laughed out loud.

I enjoyed the brightening of my relationship with Dr. Zenith. I enjoyed it thoroughly. It was a relief to nod at each other in a greeting of mutual respect in place of the cold frowns I'd received just months before.

Well, almost-mutual respect. Matthew and I received our second physics tests back. He'd earned an A. I'd run out of time and hadn't finished the last problem, so I ended up with a B. Dr. Zenith stood there in his lab and pretended to be Matthew wrestling with me and throwing me off the edge of a cliff.

No mercy.

And my house still had no kitchen.

"Be very comfortable with change throughout your life," Dr. Stillwell said on October 19th, his eyes big behind his glasses. "Because even if you aren't comfortable with it, change is going to happen."

A few days later, I got a text from my oldest stepdaughter.

"I'm coming to live with you. I'm on the bus there now."

Amber arrived on October 24th much to the delight of all, including Dr. Zenith.

CHAPTER 20

TONY THE TIGER

"Every October I'm disappointed because I didn't win a Nobel Peace Prize. And I've done so much! I haven't hit any fools!" - Dr. Zenith

Amber had been a daddy's girl, and she'd spent as much time with Randy as she could when she was little. She came to stay with us the summer she turned 12, and she lived with us the next school year too. Like Randy, Amber had an excellent head for math. Her junior year of high school she slept up in our cabin loft, doing both precalculus and trigonometry inside her little cave of refuge. Brave soul. She lived up in that loft without any complaints that the ceiling was too low and the unfinished drywall allowed spiders to creep in.

Amber and I look nothing alike. Her maternal grandmother is a Romanian Jew from Brooklyn and her paternal grandmother has Cherokee blood in her. Amber is several inches shorter than I am, with dark hair and rich olive skin, green eyes and a dimpled smile. When she lived in Hawaii with her mother and stepfather, she looked exactly the part of the dark island beauty. Yet, while our looks are as opposite as the non-twin professors, we laugh and talk together as though we're blood-related. She often says, "You're more like my big sister than my stepmother," which is true. Her father was 12 years my senior, so my stepchildren are all much older than anybody I should have birthed.

Amber joined me at school when she first arrived. "I have a plant!" Dr. Stillwell said when he spied her sitting there at one of his big black lab tables.

She slipped easily into the seat next to Mike Smith in Dr. Zenith's class that afternoon. It took all of 10 seconds for Dr. Zenith to notice the new arrival and to beckon her with his finger. Amber cheerfully hopped up to introduce herself. Did the astrophysicist abuse her and make her ashamed to be my associate? No. On the contrary, Dr. Zenith gave her permission to stay. After class, he spent a good ten minutes asking her about her life plans and encouraging her to go to college. He treated her kindly. He gave her gentle, wise advice. I stared in wonder at the two of them wrapped in a warm and friendly conversation from which I was excluded.

Wednesday evening, the fraternities hosted a trick-or-treat party for the town's children, complete with games and candy and face painting. I got my face decorated with glittery princess makeup, topped by a large jewel glued to the center of my forehead. The face paint looked so good, I didn't clean it off. I lay flat on my back all night and wore it to school the next day.

Thursday. The Thursday before Halloween. The Tony the Tiger lab day. When I am ancient and drooling into my pudding, I will still remember Dr. Zenith and the Tony the Tiger lab.

Matthew had gone off to an honor's field trip in Baltimore, so Amber sat in his seat next to me. Dr. Zenith's black shirt that day blared from his chest, "Schrödinger's Cat is Dead." I almost said, "Are you sure?" until I saw that the back of his shirt said, "Schrödinger's Cat is Not Dead."

Dr. Zenith held his role sheet and peered around the quiet room. The lesson that day was on momentum and impulse, and sadly - so sadly- a majority of the seats were empty.

"So, the rest of the class is not here," Dr. Zenith shook his head slowly. "I hate them."

"Hate is a strong word," said Mike Smith.

"Yes it is," Dr. Zenith nodded gravely. "And I am a strong man. Thank you for recognizing that."

Only eight students sat in the lab, a weak percentage of the 25 we'd had at the beginning of the semester. Many had dropped out. Matthew was off to Baltimore and Casey had gone on a soccer trip.

"Frank's gone," Dr. Zenith said. "I don't know *where* Stickley is. I just remember back at the beginning of the semester people writing me and saying they had to get into this class. Where are they now?"

Matt Griffith volunteered. "I was one of those people. Thank you."

"Good," said Dr. Zenith. "I give you three points for your appreciation of the privilege."

"Boop boop boop," Matt offered one 'boop' for each new point.

"And I'm taking away two points because you made sound effects," Dr. Zenith said.

"Boop boop," Matt's voice dropped.

Then the astrophysicist did something I have never seen before in my entire life. My entire life. He walked to one of the many drawers behind me and he pulled out two identical plastic Tony the Tiger heads. These looked like drink bottle caps or bubble bath stoppers. Amber says they were toy tops, and she should know; she saw them more closely than anybody else. They were the kinds of things that might have come out of a box of Frosted Flakes or ordered from Kellogg's with the help of two UPC symbols cut from the bottom of the cereal boxes. Whatever they were, Dr. Zenith held them up, one in each hand.

"Many people collect things," he said in his melodramatic humor mode. "I collect Tony the Tiger heads." He walked slowly around to the front of the room. "These two Tony the Tiger heads are exactly the same. Mike, do you see any differences between them?"

Mike Smith looked. "No."

"There are no differences," Dr. Zenith said coolly. "They are identical in every way. I will place this Tony the Tiger head in one cart," he raised his right hand, "and I will place this Tony the Tiger head in another, and I will send them both speeding toward a brick wall." He stopped on the other side of Mike between the two lab tables.

"But, I love this Tony the Tiger," he brandished one, then he switched hands, "and I hate this one. Love." (Brandish.) "Hate." (Brandish.)

I watched him hold up the Tony he hated, and I felt a kinship with the little plastic toy. (I know how it feels, my small tiger friend.) Amber, though. Amber had taken Matthew's place as the beloved Tony that day.

Dr. Zenith leaned on the black lab table in front of Amber, stretching across it with both Tony the Tigers held against his eyes. "Amber… Amberrr… look at me," he moved his fake orange tiger eyes in and out toward her. "Amber, you will remember this sight for the rest of your life. You'll see them in flashbacks. Amber, don't do drugs."

The full-grown astrophysicist then stood back up and said, "The Tony that I love, I buy cotton balls for that Tony. Big fluffy ones. I go down to the Rite-Aid - it's just down the road - and I go up to the counter, and I say, 'Hello Rite-Aid worker,' and he says, 'Hello Physics Professor.' (We address each other by our professions.) I ask him to help me find the biggest, fluffiest cotton balls for this Tony that I love. At Rite-Aid they have cotton balls as big as your head. Not your head, Kate. His head." Dr. Zenith pointed at the kid next to Kate. "It's bigger."

Then Dr. Zenith turned to Amber again and put the Tonys to his eyes, once again stretching them toward her. "Amberrr… during the happiest moments of your life you will see these. On your wedding night they will flash into your mind!"

Dr. Zenith continued to make Amber his Tony-top victim. And the class about died. We were laughing so hard at this display of Dr. Zenith's making the lunatic lunge, we could hardly breathe. The whole class - all eight of us and Amber - shook in our seats, hoping our hearts didn't stop.

The Tony the Tigers came up to the professor's eyes again. "Amber… Amber, your firstborn child."

In the end, the Beloved Tony the Tiger had his cart stopped by soft, fluffy cotton balls and the Hated Tony's cart ran right into an imaginary brick wall. The actual lesson? The impulse with which they stopped was equal. It didn't matter whether the cotton balls softened the blow or whether the cart ran straight into the brick wall, the Tonys experienced an equal impulse stopping their carts.

Soon we began bustling, preparing to begin the lab experiment for the day. Dr. Zenith suddenly barked about absent student Reed, who was known for saying racially insensitive things. Reed wasn't a bad guy. We all cringed when he'd make foolish, racist-sounding remarks in front of our black physics professor, but we knew he said them without any guile in his heart. He'd say things like, "Yay! I get the Asian on my team today!" referring to Tark, who was of Korean heritage. We just wished Reed would think before he spoke.

"When Reed gets back..." Dr. Zenith pointed at random people and gave orders. "You yell at him. You hit him." Then, he pointed at me. "And you mock him mercilessly."[1]

I stared in astonishment. I, the Hated Tony, I was to mock Reed mercilessly? Dr. Zenith thought I was capable of merciless mocking? I grasped those words of honor and held them to my chest! It wasn't quite as good as when he called Kate, "The Apocalyptic Pale Horse of Death," but *still*.

And then. Then he went off on my face makeup. Which I'd forgotten I was wearing.

"What!" Dr. Zenith pointed at me. "You all come in here and pretend she's normal, like nothing is different. She's all painted like an Indian princess, and I'm the one that's freaky because I've got Tony the Tiger heads!"

I laughed so much that day. Oh Matthew. Matthew, you missed that glorious Tony the Tiger lab day. You deprived soul.

Halloween fell on Sunday that year, so Dr. Zenith ordered us to dress up on Friday (that very next day). Amber got painted yellow and came as Ms. Pac-Man, pink bow and all. Matt Griffith dressed as a zombie and went around groaning, "Braaaains." Stickley returned, a big pillow up under his white lab coat. He limped into class, Igor all over. "I don't know what's wrong with me," he punned, "but I have a hunch!"

---

1   Of course, nobody yelled at Reed or hit him or mocked him mercilessly. We didn't take Dr. Zenith seriously even a little, and besides, we were not mindless attack drones.

Matthew Caerphilly, Matthew was the masterpiece. Amber covered his face and arms in black makeup and

dusted his hair and beard white. We got a black t-shirt from the thrift store and I pastel crayoned on it a white picture of a little stick guy holding up a flask in one hand and a steaming beaker in the other. It mimicked one of Dr. Zenith's black t-shirts that said, "STAND BACK. I'M GOING TO TRY SCIENCE!"

After the antagonism toward Reed the day before, I was a bit worried that Dr. Zenith would take Matthew's costume the wrong way. Nope, Matthew had dressed up as *him*, and Dr. Zenith loved it. During class, he'd call on Matthew and say, "Hey, ME. What do you think?" He even had somebody take pictures of his clone, and when his mother called and asked him for a recent picture of himself, Dr. Zenith claims to have sent her the picture of Matthew.

There are victories, and then there are just plain lovely moments. Apple cider moments. That first week of Amber's visit fits up there in the top nutmeg, pumpkin pie and whipped cream times of my whole school career.

Then came the weekend.

CHAPTER 21

SUDOKU AND THE UNIVERSE

O ver the years, Dr. Stillwell has accused me of having trust issues. "Is that why you don't trust men?" he asked me once when we wandered down the hall.

"You don't realize," I said, "that I've just gotten over resenting women."

Dr. Stillwell reads into things too much, and my trust issues are fairly mild. I simply like the freedom to investigate things. When somebody says, "Take my word for it," I have a hard time doing that. I question people without even thinking about it. I'm sure it's completely irritating, and I apologize to you in advance if I should ever do it to you.

I know I have a different worldview than is popular among scientists today. In fact, my worldview is *un*popular, to say the least. I don't think that's fair. I honestly want to figure out what is really true. Really true. So, I poke and prod and question, because the story we are told doesn't always fit what I actually see. Somebody else filtered information through their worldview, and I don't want somebody else's filtered version. I want the whole story. And that's why I have scientific trust issues.

We all have to be careful about our own biases. I do, and you do. We all do. We need to recognize their potential to color the way we interpret data and the way we regurgitate our interpretations for other people.

Stephen J. Gould does a fine job of exposing unintentional bias in his book *The Mismeasure of Man*. He describes 19th century experiments that compared the intelligence of different human groups by measuring their brain sizes. Researchers like Samuel George Morton repeatedly determined that white men had the largest skull capacity and therefore the greatest intelligence.

Of course, their results were skewed by their biases. Gould makes the case that scientists - honest, dedicated scientists - allowed their own racism to affect their measurements of skull capacity when doing research on the brain sizes of people from different continents. In order to find the capacity of a skull, the researchers would fill the skull with gunshot, and then they'd measure the volume of the shot used for each skull. It turned out that their actual data were off because researchers unconsciously filled the skulls of Anglo-Saxons to a higher level than the skulls of Africans. Shame, shame, we know your name.

What's more, the interpretation of the (poor) data fit the researchers' preconceived idea that bigger brains equaled greater intelligence. This belief wasn't justified either; Gould points out that highly intelligent people can have average or even smaller-sized brains. Because of their bias, the researchers unconsciously produced the racist results they were seeking. Near the beginning of the third chapter of *The Mismeasure of Man*, Gould states (and here's the real point):

> Science is rooted in creative interpretation. Numbers suggest, constrain, and refute; they do not, by themselves, specify the content of scientific theories. Theories are built upon the interpretation of numbers, and interpreters are often trapped by their own rhetoric. They believe in their own objectivity, and fail to discern the prejudice that leads them to one interpretation among many consistent with their numbers. Paul Broca is now distant enough. We can stand back and show that he used numbers not to generate new theories but to illustrate a priori conclusions. Shall we believe that science is different today simply because we share the cultural context of most practicing scientists and mistake its influence for objective truth?[1]

---

1 Gould, S. J. (1993). *The Mismeasure of Man* (pg. 74). New York: W.W. Norton & Company.

Dr. Gould, I bow in your general direction. Thank you.

One of the biggest questions we have as humans is, "How did we get here?" Where did the universe come from? How did Earth get to be here? This is one area where our presuppositions absolutely can color our interpretations of data.

I picked up my first book on cosmology when I was 21. It's a fun little area of study for me, even though most of it is *way* beyond my pay grade. Still, hunting into the origins of the universe has made something clear to me: there are a lot of mysteries out there. Lots and lots of mysteries. Astrophysicists can measure the cosmic microwave background (CMB). They can gather terabytes of light wave data from distant supernovae and quasars. They speculate about dark matter and black holes. They have discussions about how the universe might have inflated within the first fraction of a second after the Big Bang. All the raw data don't in themselves force a single undeniable conclusion about the nature of the universe.

Fun fact. It was the Roman Catholic priest Monsignor Georges Lemaître who in 1927 first suggested that the universe was expanding, based on certain solutions to Einstein's field equations. Two years later, Lemaître's expanding universe got a boost when Edwin Hubble published a report on the redshift, stating that the redshift of light from distant galaxies was proportional to how far that light had traveled - that is, the distances of those galaxies from us when the light left them. Together, these things indicated that the galaxies and the stars in them were all flying out into space away from a single point, which led to the idea of the Big Bang.

I'm entertained by this, because the cosmological community initially rejected the idea of a Big Bang. They had been using Einstein's static (unchanging) universe model, in which the universe was infinite in time, but finite in space. The new idea from Lemaître and Hubble was shocking because it meant the universe had a beginning, which fit with the idea that God had created the universe at a specific moment in time. This concerned a variety of scientists who saw the Big Bang as a creationist model, and it took awhile for the cosmologists of the day to accept it. Of course, today's young earth creationists are among those who reject the Big Bang because it suggests a 13.8 billion-year-old universe, and they don't think the universe is that old. I find this little view reversal ironic and it makes me smile.

Note something, though. It doesn't matter whether the Big Bang is a creationist model or not! It doesn't matter! The issue is whether the Big Bang model best explains the observations we can make about the universe. That's what matters.

The Big Bang is widely accepted now because it fits important pieces of evidence - primarily the existence of the CMB radiation and the expanding appearance of the universe. Still. Nothing is easy or simple, and there are some odd facts about the universe that are hard to explain. Two of the big puzzles are called the "horizon" and "flatness" problems.

The horizon problem has to do with how smooth the universe is. Basically, the cosmic microwave background is homogenous throughout the visible universe. It's the same temperature everywhere we look, which is peculiar. The CMB is regarded as the electromagnetic radiation residue of the Big Bang, and we'd expect it to have some clumpy areas, but the radiation has reached equilibrium across the whole sky as far as we can see. According to the Big Bang timescale, there hasn't been enough time for the light to radiate into equilibrium across the universe, but the CMB didn't get the memo because it's homogenous anyway. That's the horizon problem.

The flatness problem isn't so much a problem, I guess, as just a really odd coincidence. We live in a flat universe, which is very convenient for us, because it means we get to exist. If the density of mass and energy in the universe were much greater, the fabric of space-time would curve in on itself and it would all rush back together in a "Big Crunch." If the density were less, the fabric of space-time would curve the other way, all matter and energy would shoot off away into the nothing, and it would end in a "Big Chill." However, the density of our universe is very near the critical density required to keep the universe flat - which means it would have been smack equal to the critical density back at the Big Bang. That's much too coincidental for the cosmologists to let slide.

There's also the monopole and entropy problems, not to mention *what* caused the expansion in the first place. My goal here is not to torment anybody with details. I just want to note the fact that there are puzzles - puzzles that don't fit the simple model.

Aren't the cosmologists working to address these issues?

Absolutely. Alan Guth introduced the idea of inflation back in 1980 to answer the horizon, flatness, and monopole problems, and brilliant sorts like Andrei Linde and Paul Steinhardt joined him.[2] The inflationary model says the universe swelled from the size of a subatomic particle to the size of a softball in a fraction of a second - pop! In that tiny slice of time, the freaked-out quantum world stretched and smoothed and flattened, and by the time the initial inflation slowed down, the universe was able to expand evenly. This is the current favorite fix for the horizon and flatness problems. Of course, there's always got to be troublemakers, and Paul Steinhardt (who helped develop the inflationary theory in the first place) now argues it causes more problems than it answers. Steinhardt told *Scientific American:*

> The whole point of inflation was to get rid of fine-tuning - to explain features of the original big bang model that must be fine-tuned to match observations. The fact that we had to introduce one fine-tuning to remove another was worrisome. This problem has never been resolved.

> But my concerns really grew when I discovered that, due to quantum fluctuation effects, inflation is generically eternal and (as others soon emphasized) this would lead to a multiverse. Inflation was introduced to produce a universe that looks

2   Guth, A. (1981). Inflationary Universe: A Possible Solution to the Horizon and Flatness Problems. *Physical Review D*, 23:347 // Guth, A. (2007). Eternal Inflation and Its Implications. *Journal of Physics A: Mathematical and Theoretical* 40:6811–6826 //Linde, A. (1982). A New Inflationary Universe Scenario: A Possible Solution of the Horizon, Flatness, Homogeneity, Isotropy and Primordial Monopole Problems. *Physics Letters B*, 108 (6): 389-393// Albrecht, A. and Steinhardt, P. (1982). Reheating an Inflationary Universe. *Physical Review Letters*, 48:1437.

smooth and flat everywhere and that has features everywhere that agree with what we observe. Instead, it turns out that, due to quantum effects, inflation produces a multitude of patches (universes) that span every physically conceivable outcome… Scientific ideas should be simple, explanatory, predictive. The inflationary multiverse as currently understood appears to have none of those properties. [3]

I loved Paul Steinhardt for this bold honesty, and I wanted to marry him. Then, I learned that he already had a wife and is old enough to be my father… and lives in New Jersey. I guess it wasn't meant to be.

Inflation's not the only fix-it for the Big Bang. In 1999 Andreas Albrecht and João Magueijo started trying something else - a varying speed of light model. As an alternative to inflation, they suggested that the speed of light was vastly faster there at the beginning of the universe, before light slowed to its present rate.[4] J.W. Moffat at the University of Toronto had been independently making a similar case since 1993.[5] I am deeply enamored of this idea, and with João Magueijo (a Portuguese cutie!!), and I want to see where it goes. If light were nearly instantaneous at the beginning, then it could have spread out evenly across space in no time.

The whole point I'm making here is *not* that my heart goes pitter-pat over bold cosmologists and their ideas. That… that's not a good point. I'll never get a boyfriend. My point is that there are still mysteries!! The Big Bang model is like a muscle shirt that doesn't quite fit, and the cosmologists are trying to tailor it to work. The inflationary patch is the favorite fix for it right now, but that

---

3   Horgan, J. (2014). Physicist Slams Cosmic Theory He Helped Conceive. *Scientific American*, last accessed January 24, 2018 at https://blogs.scientificamerican.com/cross-check/physicist-slams-cosmic-theory-hehelped-conceive/.

4   Barrow, J.D. (1999). Cosmologies with Varying Light Speed, *Physical Review D* 59:043515 // Albrecht, A., & Magueijo, J. (1999). Time Varying Speed of Light as a Solution to Cosmological Puzzles. *Physical Review D*, 59:043516// Magueijo, J. (2003). *Faster Than the Speed of Light: The Story of a Scientific Speculation.* Cambridge, MA: Perseus Book Group.// Magueijo, J. & Moffat, J.W. (2008). Comments on "Note on Varying Speed of Light Theories." *General Relativity and Gravitation* 40:1797–1806 // Afshordi, N. & Magueijo, J. (2016). The Critical Geometry of a Thermal Big Bang. *Physical Review D* 94:101301.

5   Moffat, J.W. (1993) Superluminary Universe: A Possible Solution to the Initial Value Problem in Cosmology, *Int. J. Mod. Phys. D* 2:351-365 // Moffat, J.W. (1993) Quantum Gravity, the Origin of Time and Time's Arrow, *Found. Phys.* 23: 411-437. // Moffat, J.W. (2016). Variable Speed of Light Cosmology, Primordial Fluctuations and Gravitational Waves. *European Physical Journal* C 76:130.

might change. I recognize that it's not so easy to figure out what exactly happened at the beginning of the universe. I also know that figuring things out is part of the fun of the whole thing. That's why people become cosmologists or cosmogonists or astrophysicists; they like discovering things and solving puzzles. We can give them space.[6]

However, when we the public are told the 6th grade version of the history of the universe, nobody bothers to tell us "By the way, this thing over here doesn't fit. We have parts leftover." Nobody warns us.

Check out the solar nebula hypothesis, for instance. I think it's fair to pick on this one just a little bit.

NEBULAR THEORY

How did our solar system get here? The standard explanation is that the planets formed from clumpy bits of the dusty cloud – the solar nebula - that shot away from our busily collapsing young sun. The solar nebular theory (SNT) explains why the planets all revolve around the sun in the same direction and why they're all on the same plane in their orbits. However, there are some other things that are troubling about the theory.[7] At the very least, the solar system is much messier than we'd expect, and a lot of difficult realities have to be explained. Cosmogonists are working hard to figure things out and to develop models that explain the messiness, but the theory has so many wrenches in it, all I can see are handles, handles sticking out everywhere.

The space scholars haven't given up, of course. The SNT has put a lot of people to work on computers, modeling possible explanations for why Uranus (*with* its moons) is on its side, rotating backwards, and how Neptune even exists at all, and why Venus is apparently upside down and why there's a heck of a lot more oxygen in the sun than in the Earth or the Moon or Mars.

Then, there's the faint young sun problem.[8] When the Earth was supposed to have formed from the solar nebula 4.5 billion years ago, the sun would have been much less bright, which means the

---

6   Haha… puns are so fun.
7   See "The Solar Nebular Theory" in the Appendix.
8   See "The Solar Nebular Theory" in the Appendix, and scroll down a bit.

Earth should have been too cold for liquid water to exist during its first couple billion years. Yet, there are bacteria in Archean rocks dated 3.8-2.5 billion years ago, which means there was liquid water.

What's that all about?

There are skilled people working hard to answer the faint sun problem, along with all the other problems, but nothing so far has worked. That's okay. Folks are still looking for the answers. That's what they're supposed to be doing.

Figure 20 - A sudoku puzzle waiting to be solved.

The reason I'm making a big deal about cosmological problems is because they always make me think of Sudoku. If you haven't tried a Sudoku puzzle, you really should sit down and pencil one out. The trick with Sudoku is to be patient and leave spots empty until you figure out what each number has to be. It's no good to fill in numbers just because they can fit, because one incorrectly placed digit will end up gumming up the whole thing. A five was stuck in the spot where a two should go. Backtracking is required.

Numbers can almost always be placed by logic, without guessing, but sometimes a bold move is necessary. If that bold move was a mistake, reverse and try something else. Perhaps an occasional genius eye can fill in the gaps in one glance, but for the rest of us mortals it's not so easy.

8	5	3	2	7	9	6	4	1
1	4	7			3	2		9
6	2	9	4	8	1	3	7	5
9	7	2	3		4	1	6	
4	8	6	1	5	7	9	2	3
3	1	5	6	9	2	4	8	7
2	3	1	5	4	8	7	9	6
7	6	4	9	1		8	3	2
	9	8	7	6		5	1	4

8	2	3	5	7	9	6	4	1
1	5	7	4	3	6	2	9	8
6	4	9	8	2	1	3	7	5
9	7	2	3	8	4	1	5	6
4	8	6	1	5	7	9	2	3
3	1	5	6	9	2	4	8	7
5	3	1	2	4	8	7	6	9
7	6	4	9	1	5	8	3	2
2	9	8	7	6	3	5	1	4

Figure 21 - Compare the puzzle on the left to the completed puzzle on the right. The rows and columns on the right are filled without any conflict, because all numbers were placed exactly where they actually belonged. Boom. No holes.

I wonder sometimes how many scientific models are developed with plenty of facts fitting neatly into place for a time. When things pop up that don't fit, though, do the scientists readily tear apart their model and start again? Or do they focus on the numbers that look like they belong, ignore the big gaps, and try to force their idea to work without realizing that their model has fundamental flaws? The universe doesn't care about our philosophies about what *has* to be. Our solar system has an actual, unchanging history. If a model describing that history is truly correct, then all the pieces will eventually fit neatly into place. If it requires too much wrenching, it might just need to be rebuilt.

So, I have trust issues about the common answers to common questions. I have confidence that scientists are truly looking for the best answers to the problems that face them. I do. However, if the best ideas we have don't work, what are the possible alternatives?

In the meanwhile, it doesn't hurt to find a field somewhere, lie down, and just stare up at the stars.

CHAPTER 22

FOXES IN THE VINEYARD

Catch us the foxes, The little foxes that spoil the vines, For our vines have tender grapes.

Song of Songs 2:15

The handyman's voice demanded that I pay attention: "Amy, you were robbed!" Eight times. Eight different voicemails, as though I didn't hear the first seven. All the same steady, insistent message. "Amy. You were robbed!" I can still hear it, drubbed into my brain with repetition. The robbery upset Gary, really fried him, and it took me two days to hear the awesome news because I'd let my phone die.

The robbery began my packed, not-especially-pleasant weekend. Some local degenerates had broken into my workshop and cleaned me out. They busted through the locked shop door and they took everything; my power tools and big air compressor, the table saw we got Randy for Christmas and the miter saw we gave him for his 40th birthday. They took everything of value. I think they left my spade for me. We'll pretend they were being kind.

It turned out to be pretty depressing. The sheriff wasn't able to take fingerprints because of the dusty nature of the shop, and I had no serial numbers in my files, so I had no way of hunting down the stolen tools. Worst of all, my insurance wouldn't cover the loss. I'd probably have been more upset if Gary hadn't done all the flipping out for me.

Then, there were the lice. I hadn't known exactly what lice looked like, but I'd known there was something crawling among Sammy's

153

locks. Even after buzzing their heads, the eggs were so thickly packed across my boys' tiny stumps of hair I ended up just shaving Sam and Zeke bald, skinhead style. I had treated myself and Savannah too, but Amber confirmed we were still infected. I had to wash everything and take all the blankets and sheets and pillows down to the laundromat. Amber carefully pulled the nits from my hair while I sat in the bathroom trying to read my Cell Biology notes.

Aside from the attacks by lice and rotten thieves, it was Halloween weekend, and I had small children to dress and take out. On a good note, Gary and I were able to drive into Alexandria and pick up that stove and fridge and dishwasher and cupboards the lady wanted to sell to me for $700. That was the weekend we did it.

All these fun things, and I had big exams in Physics and in Cell Biology on Monday. Important exams. I had to study! In every spare spot of time I tried to study for those exams. I read notes in the back of the chilly van while Gary drove us to Alexandria, and Amber read them to me on the way to school. I stayed up until midnight studying physics with Matthew and woke up at 5am to study more. I skipped my other classes Monday morning to read and read and read until it was time for those two tests.

I won an A on the Physics exam. In Cell Biology, I pulled out a C.

"You got a C? That's good!" Katz said after that horrific Cell test.

"Yeah, but I got an A on the last one," I said.

Katz was disgusted with me. "You're a nice person," she said, "but you have a B in the class. The rest of us all failed, so you need to go away."

I suppose they'd have wanted straight-A Maggie to go away too, but she's smart enough to keep her mouth shut.

But, yeah. I had skipped my other classes that Monday morning, the morning after Halloween, and it got Dr. Stillwell miffed at me.

"So!" Dr. S. said to me on Tuesday during lab. "You were out partying late on Halloween and you couldn't make it to class yesterday."

"No, sir," I muttered. "I was not partying."

"Uh huh. You had sooo many things that were more important."

"No," I said again. "I just had a really difficult weekend. The kids had lice, and I had to get my kitchen from Alexandria, and I had to talk to the sheriff because I was robbed, and I had to get Amber from her grandmother's…"

I still didn't want to admit to him I'd skipped his class to study for another one. Another two classes. He had to know, though, that I wouldn't have done so without some desperation. I'd seriously needed that extra study time or I'd have been smashed flat.

Dr. Stillwell didn't let it go. He was still irritated, and he grouched at me again by the rock saw a little later.

"…Since it's so hard for you to get to class…"

As he complained, a realization struck me. I thought about that dream I'd had about him - *the* dream - and a light shone on my understanding. My eyes opened wide, and I stared at him. "You *missed* me!" I said, suddenly recognizing the true source of his irritation.

Ha! That's what it was!

I nodded at my professor. "You missed me over the weekend, and you were looking forward to seeing me on Monday, and I wasn't there!"

He didn't deny it. He just looked grumpy, his chin down and his eyebrows all scrunched. "Well, class isn't the same without you," he grumbled.

HAHA! HA HA AHA HA. HA! That was the sound my heart made. I wanted to laugh out loud.

"You know," I told him the next day, "you should have said, 'Amy Joy, you missed class. What's wrong? It must have been something awful for you to have missed my class.'"

He chuckled and admitted, "Okay. I should have been worried about you."

It's true.

Dr. Stillwell worked hard to maintain his appropriate teacher distance, but I saw through him. I saw through that straight-edged old man and his professionalism. The dream told me something else - it told me his care for me was warm, but innocent. A good, warm, comfortable emotion. It was precious. It might have been the most important thing the dream told me, because that kind of relationship is a rare find in our world.

That same week, Dr. Stillwell stopped into our physics lab to ask Dr. Zenith a question.

"Hello Dr. Stillwell," I grinned. "It's a pleasure to see you!"

For a moment, his eyes brightened. Then he frowned and turned away from me. He asked Dr. Zenith if he would be willing to teach summer classes the next year.

"No," Dr. Zenith said without guilt. Dr. Zenith feels no obligations; he is a free agent.

As Dr. Stillwell turned to leave, he reached out to pat my arm. He reached out - Matthew and Amber both noticed it too - but then he stopped. He dropped his arm, and he left the classroom.

Dr. Zenith and Dr. Stillwell both kept a barrier between themselves and their students. Teachers have to maintain that protective distance for a lot of reasons. Some students can get scary, first of all. Professors have stories of being stalked at their houses, of having students who just won't go away. Even without going as far as stalking, students can hang around too much and waste their educators' valuable time. Bad situations of all kinds can erupt if teachers and students get too close, which is obvious these days when we read about some scandal or another. But, perhaps the most common problem that a teacher faces is caring about students and losing them, year after year after year. It's hard to teach for 25 years and watch your kids leave and never come back.

Professors are wise to maintain a friendly arm's-length between themselves and the young people they teach. Dr. Stillwell was having a problem. He cared about me, and the bricks kept coming loose in the center of the wall between us.

He paid attention to me. He even worried about me. He noticed when I came to class looking less-than-well. He gave one of his cruel and unusual tests the Wednesday after Halloween, and I'd suffered another sleepless night. "How are things going?" he asked me as I handed in my exam. My eyes were red from exhaustion, and I must have looked pretty wretched, because he answered his question himself. "Not real well, huh?"

"Thank you for asking," I said, because I knew he meant it. "The answer to that question is always going to be the same. In the big scheme of things, I'm just fine."

"But the devil is in the details," he finished.

I nodded.

I was grateful for the fact that he saw my condition and offered some compassion. I wanted him to know that I felt fine, despite thieving foxes in my vineyard. The surface of my life suffered a lot of noise, but inside I enjoyed a solid, steady contentment.

Although, I can get myself into trouble just fine too.

CHAPTER 23

THE SILLY FIB

I had worked hard to make peace with Dr. Zenith: paying obvious attention in his class, doing well on his strictly-timed tests, turning in my lab reports with disciplined promptness, and of course *not* dropping out along with half the class. As Matthew wisely noted, "Dr. Zenith doesn't reward effort, he rewards obedience." I had to dig for every scrap of respect from the astrophysicist, every little shredded fragment. He didn't offer his regard without blood and bruises, and I was loathe to screw things up with him.

It was the Thursday of that same painful week. Thursday, November 4th, the same day Anne Eugénie Blanchard died at the age of 114, the 15th anniversary of the assassination of Yitzhak Rabin. Just a weary day.

I dropped into Dr. Stillwell's office guest chair for a moment after getting some details worked out with Flash about the next semester. I sat there in the good doctor's chair, drained to my ankles. I had only enough energy to fill my holey size 9 ½ Chuck Taylors, but still I had work to get done and turned in.

Dr. S. and I bantered for a minute or two, then I said, "Well. I have to go get a report done for Dr. Zenith. It's due today."

Dr. Stillwell's eyes opened wide. "You'd *better* get it done, or he'll hurt you."

"I know," I nodded. I had a couple of hours to finish it, and Dr. Zenith's lab reports were not long.

I heaved myself up and trudged up to the computer lab. The lab report took longer than I'd hoped, though, and I progressively worked faster and faster. I kept my eyes on the clock, and as the minutes ticked by, I realized that I wasn't going to be able to finish the percent errors portion of the report in time. If I tried, I'd be late, and I had promised Dr. Zenith that wouldn't happen again after the Beating with Cookies. It would take me only five more minutes, but I didn't have five minutes.

I considered whether I could pencil out a page of percent errors at the beginning of class. I could... just... pull my report back out of the pile and attach the extra page to the back. Quickly. My class grade quivered on the edge between an A and a B; I needed every point.

No. Shoot. I'd just have to deal with a lower grade on that assignment.

I printed off the report *without* the percent errors, and I trotted down the stairs to class.

I stuck my paper into its place in the pile on time, and I sat in my chair.

Unfortunately, efficiency sweats from Dr. Zenith's pores. As soon as he had set up our lab for the day, he sat down with our alphabetically arranged reports and graded them. He could have given them back at the end of the class period if he'd wanted, but he didn't. He always waited until the next week.

Matthew and Mike and I proceeded with our lab assignment for the day. We stood at the black lab table counting spring oscillations when Dr. Zenith beckoned to me.

"Amy Joy," he said.

I went over to him.

He pointed to the blank section of my paper. "Where are the percent errors? I mean, you say in your conclusion that your percent error is high."

Crud. I'd put that in as a place holder until I'd had the actual errors calculated. I'd forgotten to take it out, because I didn't actually know whether they were high or not.

I stuttered. "Th - they're... Um. On the computer upstairs."

"Why are they not here?" Dr. Zenith asked.

"Because, I, uh… didn't … um… it's not…" I stumbled around. The percent errors were not actually on the computer upstairs. Not yet. If I could get up there, though, I knew I could get them off that computer. That's not what I said out loud, but it was what I was thinking. It was about potential. Physicists know all about potential.

Now, this shows just how much my relationship with Dr. Zenith had improved. Two months prior, he would have just marked off those points. He would have frowned at me and criticized and expressed disgust. That's not what he did that November 4th.

He interrupted my stuttering and said, "You can lose a few points and go upstairs and get those percent errors to me, or you can*not* get them and lose a lot of points."

"Okay," I brightened.

"Class ends at 3:00. I'll give you until 3:15 to bring them down."

"Okay," I said. "I can do that."

I finished up my graph about spring oscillations. I handed it to the physics prof and packed my books into my bag. At 3:00 I walked calmly out of the room and down the hall, and then I bolted up to the computer lab to calculate those percent errors as fast as my fingers could fly. I printed them out, and I marched down to Dr. Zenith's office, reading through them all the way.

Darn. I'd done them wrong. I'd been in too much of a hurry.

I had already been feeling bad for my fib earlier. It was just as well I'd muffed it, because I began to feel it was better not handing in the paper at all. When he'd given Matthew and me our reports after the Beating with Cookies, he'd only dropped us a letter grade. I knew he'd only take off a few points for doing the calculations wrong. That wasn't even the issue, though. I felt dishonest.

I sludged up to Dr. Zenith. "I didn't do them right," I said.

"It's okay," he reached out for my paper.

I started to crumple it. "No. It's … they're not right."

He wanted them anyway. He wanted to accept my calculations, even if they were late and incorrect. He wanted to allow me to turn in all my material to him. He wanted to be *gracious* to me.

I handed them over and left, struggling in my guts.

I had deceived him. Even if it wasn't completely a lie… it was a lie. It was a deception. I hadn't had my work done. I didn't deserve to hand anything in at all, right or wrong.

"But it was upstairs in the computer," Dr. Stillwell took my side when I told him about it later. "All you had to do was go up and get it."

All I had to do was push the keys, and the percent errors would come out! ("Where is that statue you promised me, Michelangelo?" "Give me a minute! I just have to go get it out of this mountain!")

"That's what I thought," I answered Dr. Stillwell. "But he wouldn't have accepted it if he knew the truth."

Daggone it. That's what Randy would have said. "Daggone it."

I met Matthew and Amber outside. I couldn't go fess up to Dr. Zenith about such a stupid little thing! What should I do?

"You don't need to tell him," Amber said, adamant. This was Dr. Zenith! Dr. Zenith who would have thrown away my phone two months earlier. Dr. Zenith the astrophysicist, who despised me for so long, who got on my case for not pushing in my *chair*.

I had a bigger problem, though. Okay, it's not really a problem, but it can definitely feel like an inconvenience. I know that I don't belong to myself. I serve the God of Eternity, and I represent Him. It didn't matter if no other human knew that I had lied to Dr. Zenith, God and I and the whole eternal cast of witnesses knew. When King David slept with Bathsheba and had her husband killed, he ruined lives. He also brought great shame on the reputation of the God he had served so faithfully. He had given the enemies of God cause to blaspheme, to insult and ridicule Him. David was the king, and he could have gotten away with it as far as the legal system of the day went, but there's more to serving God than the legal system of the day.

I hadn't stolen anybody's spouse. I hadn't killed anybody. But, I had compromised my integrity, and even as I stood there and tried to justify it, I knew it was just a weak and cheap thing to have done. Small and understandable, but shame on me just the same.

I feel like a jerk writing about this. Too many people are thinking, "You fibbed to Dr. Zenith about some stupid percent errors? Big deal. I shouldn't even print some of the things I've done." We've *all* done much worse things. That's not the point. The point is that… big or small, it was still wrong.

"Let it go," Amber urged me. "It's okay."

After all the work I'd done to get a smidgen of respect, I wanted to let it go. It had been so hard, and I still felt like I was on shaky ground. I didn't want to go up and admit I'd fibbed to him, to *him*, Dr. Zenith of all people!!

"I have to do it," I told them. "Pray for me."

So, Friday after the class lecture, I approached my physics professor at his PowerPoint station. "Can I talk to you?" I asked.

"Sure," Dr. Zenith said simply.

I followed him to his office, rehearsing all the things I wanted to say, but when we got there, I just dumped out a scattering of sentence fragments.

"I hadn't finished. That's why it wasn't there. The percent errors," I said.

He nodded. He did not look super surprised.

"I apologize. I want you to take off those extra points. I was an ass. I apologize."

Dr. Zenith smiled the tiniest bit at the, "I was an ass," part.

"You're better than that," he said.

"I *am*," I nodded.

"It's always better to be honest," he said. "It's not worth a few extra points to compromise."

"I agree," I said.

He nodded in understanding. "Thank you for your honesty. That says something about you too."

That was the extent of it. I nodded and left.

I headed outside where Matthew waited to patch up my wounds.

"I thought you were going to talk to Dr. Zenith!" he said.

"I did!" I said.

"Wow. That was fast."

Yeah, and thank God it was over.

It was a small thing, but it didn't matter, because it would have been worse to get away with it. I've decided that I don't like justifying even small lies. It's not that I don't fall into them, because sometimes I do. But, I always feel rotten about it. I'd rather pay the extra $10 for the tickets, walk the extra two blocks, miss out on the free drink, or give up a few points than try to justify something I'm not proud of.

"You and Dr. Zenith have a very interesting relationship," Dr. Stillwell said when I told him about the whole thing.

"It makes a good story at least," I said.

"I like your stories," he said.

I certainly hope so. Because I'm telling them to the whole world...

CHAPTER 24

VISIONS

Lance (child):	Here. You can have the rest of my shake.
Baron (adult):	Thanks.
Lance:	Is that good?
Baron:	Yes. Yes, it is.
Lance:	See? Now you know it existed.

D r. Stillwell used his PowerPoint station to draw contour lines on a topographic map. "Chugga chugga chugga chugga. Sound effects help with this stuff," he said. "Does this seem a bit tedious? Welcome to the world of map making."

I cared about Dr. Stillwell. I enjoyed his class. I enjoyed his cautious friendship. I wanted to tell him the things that God had said to me about him, but I couldn't.

I prayed for him all the time.

"When I pray for you-" I started to tell Dr. S. months later.

"What do you pray for me?" he interrupted, his eyes eager.

"All I can pray is, 'Thank you for loving him, Lord. *Thank you for loving him.*"

"See!" Dr. Stillwell exclaimed, pleased.

I thought he meant, "See? That's why I tolerate you and your faith. You're not filled with nasty contempt for other people. You don't look down on others. You don't assume I'm an evil sinner needing to be saved."

Dr. Stillwell didn't understand. I praised God for loving my professor because it was the only thing that I could do. I mean, I asked Him to reveal Himself to Dr. Stillwell and to forgive him.

I asked those things too. But, mostly, I hunted around spiritually, trying to find the thing that needed to be prayed for him. Those are the prayers God seems to bless, but it's frustrating when I can't find the right thing. There's no life in my spirit regarding any words I say. At that point, I have to be patient and wait for God to show me.

With Dr. Stillwell, there was nothing I really could do but say, "Thank you for loving him. *Thank you* for loving him!" And when I would praise God for already loving Dr. Stillwell, joy would fill my spirit.

How fun is that! The interesting thing to me was that the more I thanked God for loving Dr. Stillwell, the more delighted Dr. Stillwell seemed to be with me. I don't know what spiritual things go on when we praise God, but I think spiritual things do go on.

Still. I could not talk to Dr. Stillwell about religious matters. Nope. Not Dr. Zenith either. The cross-campus conversation with Dr. Derlidger had taken place despite the fact that I didn't want it, and even though I wanted to talk to Dr. Stillwell about the things God was doing in me, I didn't get to.

When I was about 9-years-old, I lay awake at night imagining that all the other children were gathered around Jesus while I was left out. In my mind, I stood off to the side while they laughed with him and enjoyed him. I felt rejected. I always felt rejected. Then, something inside me said, "No. You're not left out. He wants you too." After that, I imagined he'd gather me up in his arms and hold me close, and that always made me cry. Every night for months I imagined him holding me close. I don't think God wants anybody left out.

I don't care if people believe the same things I do for my own sake. I don't care. Why should I? Yes, it's nice to talk to somebody who understands me, who is already on the same page as I am. There's a lot of peace in that. However, I also appreciate different viewpoints. I like hanging out with people who make me say, "Wow. I hadn't thought of it like that before." I have little interest in controlling other people, and I know God is big and can handle them Himself. If He wants to involve me, that's exciting. But, it isn't about me at all.

At the same time, I want people to know how good God is. I want them to know that He's real and they matter to Him. I don't want them to die without Him, and I don't want anybody to be left out when God loves them so much. God loved Dr. Stillwell for some reason, and it was a shame that he didn't know it.

God kept doing things that fall semester. Here I was, a science student, and God kept poking His finger through the dimensions I couldn't see right into my little domain. I kept wanting to tell Dr. Stillwell about the things God was showing me, but nope nope nope. No opportunities. No.

No, God told me to wait for Him. In fact, He gave me a very interesting verse:

> *Therefore the LORD will wait, that He may be gracious to you; And therefore He will be exalted, that He may have mercy on you. For the LORD is a God of justice; Blessed are all those who wait for Him. And though the Lord gives you The bread of adversity and the water of affliction, Yet your teachers will not be moved into a corner anymore, But your eyes shall see your teachers. Your ears shall hear a word behind you, saying, "This is the way, walk in it," Whenever you turn to the right hand Or whenever you turn to the left.*
>
> -Isaiah 30:18, 20-21

I read that, and I wanted to throw my Bible across the room.

I could handle the part about waiting, and the bread of adversity was nothing new. Water of affliction? The story of my life, thank you. The part that upset me was the promise that my teachers would not be removed into a corner anymore, that I would see them, and that God would direct me and tell me what to do.

The Bible is not my personal fortune cookie. I couldn't use it that way! "How do I know that that's really from You!" I asked God. "How can I know? I *want* You to direct me. I don't want to lose my teachers anymore. How do I know it's not just my wishful thinking!" I don't think I actually flung the Bible. I don't think I did, but I pictured it in my head.

Then, on November 7th, Amber and Matt Griffith ("boop boop boop") and the kids and I drove down to Potomac, Maryland to pull up hardwood flooring from the old house about to be torn down. We spent all day with pry bars, jimmying up that perfectly good oak flooring and loading it into my van. I was pinched and banged and scraped, but we had collected solid wood for my cabin.

Bruised and weary, Amber, Matt, the kids and I climbed back into the van. (Thank you for your help, you guys!) We then set off to pick up a free exterior door in Rockville, and darkness had set in by the time we headed back up I-270 through Maryland.

There weren't many people on the road that Sunday evening. Matt and Amber and the little ones huddled together in the back of the unheated van. I bounced up and down in the driver's seat, trying to stay warm. The phone rang, and I answered it.

It was Matthew. "Hey," he said. "I just wanted to call and let you know that God gave me two visions about you."

"Really?" I shivered in the dark front seat, my breath misting in the cold. I've never had visions. Randy had visions. Matthew had visions too. "What were they?" I asked.

"In the first one," Matthew said, "you were sitting on God's lap, sobbing with your heart broken. You cried and cried and God held you. Then after awhile you stopped crying, and God set you down and wiped your nose. The burden hadn't gone away, but you were okay. You could bear it. Then a light shot from His hand and He split a mountain behind you and He gave you a little push down that path toward the split in the mountain."

Matthew said I didn't want to go. I didn't want to walk that path. But when I saw that God was over there on the other side, I was ready to go. Then God gave me a teddy bear to hug as I took this hard path. (That part really moved Matthew.)

"The second vision wasn't as clear, because I was distracted," Matthew went on. "But you were full of light and fire, and God was directing you very closely. Turn right. Turn left. And you were following His directions well. Then I heard a voice say, 'And it was Thursday.'"

There it was again, the whole "This is the way, walk ye in it," verse from Isaiah.

"Thank you, Matthew," I told him. Both of those visions had a personal meaning to me. Both touched on things in my history. And apparently, in my future.

CHAPTER 25

HORSE ACCIDENT

I t was the day that my little sister Whitney and I took a drive into the mountains and saw turkeys. I tried drinking green bean juice straight from the can, and I decided it wasn't bad at all. It was that day, March, 1999, when Randy and I were still just friends.

As Whitney and I drove along, my pager buzzed. Then it buzzed again - a long message. I looked at the numbers: 436107363727293. "IM SORRY" in simple pager code.

I couldn't make out the rest of Randy's message very well - he was at work and in a hurry, and he messed up some numbers. Something about a horse.

"What were you sorry for?" I asked Randy that evening. "I couldn't understand the rest of the page you sent."

"Oh," Randy said. "It was about your horse accident. God gave me a vision of your horse accident, and it was really bad, and I'm sorry I was rude to you about it."

Earlier that week, I had started to tell him about how I'd been stepped on by my horse when I was 15. Randy had brushed me off like I was annoying. "I've been stepped on by horses too," he said.

Now, two days later, his whole attitude had changed. "I was standing at my machine," he said, "and the Lord gave me a vision of your horse accident. I saw the whole thing, and it was bad, and I'm sorry. I shouldn't have acted like that. I just wanted to tell you I was sorry."

I didn't think much about it at the time - about Randy's having a vision. I had no reason to question it. Randy had apologized for something that I hadn't even fussed about, something I'd let go.

When he first told me about the vision, I just thought, "Wow. God stuck up for me. Thanks, God!"

It *did* matter months later when Randy started talking about marriage. That's when it got serious, because a crazy husband is a much different thing than a crazy friend. I had to know, did Randy really have visions? Was he a nutcase? Did he have oxygen deficiency issues? Did he eat too much sauerkraut? Was he just trying to get attention? I didn't have a problem with the idea that God gave people visions; I just needed to know if Randy's visions were legitimate.

"Father," I said to God. "Is he for real?" A moment later, I remembered that horse vision.

"All right," I told Randy as we drove across the prairie the next night. "Remember when you saw my horse accident? Tell me what the horse looked like."

Randy said, "Well, it was a really big, dark horse. Much bigger than I thought it would be."

And she was. My horse Bourbon was an American Saddlebred, almost 17 hands high. That's huge for an animal that's not a draft horse.

"Okay," I said. "Tell me what happened. Describe what you saw."

"You were up on her," Randy said, "and something spooked her. She reared up, and then she twisted around and fell, and it looked like she landed on you. Then she got up, but I couldn't see what was going on with you on the ground."

What was going on with me is that when Bourbon got up, she walked all over my legs. She *stepped on me*, like I'd tried to tell Randy. She left beautiful purple and black horseshoe-shaped bruises on my shins and calves. After she tore off through the woods, I managed to get up and limp over to a log to sit down, my legs shaking like an old engine. Nothing had broken. I wasn't crushed. My lower back still despises me, but I was okay.

Randy's description of the accident was accurate, more accurate than I'd remembered. I'd forgotten about Bourbon's twisting around, but he was right. She had twisted in the air when she'd fallen.

[Interjection by my brother Shadow: "The horse didn't just step on her. Gosh, Amy tells things so vanilla sometimes. There was a wolf dog attacking the horse with Amy on her, and the horse just freaked out. Bourbon reared up and fell over, and then she got up and was kicking and stomping, terrified and fighting for her life. It was like rodeo's worst moments on YouTube. You have this little girl getting stomped by this huge horse who is jumping around in terror, trying to *kill her*."]

[Thank you Shadow.]

"Okay," I asked Randy next, "what did the saddle look like?"

Randy got all uncomfortable when I asked that.

"You know," he said. "It was just to show me that I shouldn't have treated you like that. It was just to show me that it was a bad accident."

"Randy," I said, "what did the saddle look like?"

He shrugged, tense and embarrassed. Then he repeated himself, insisting that it was just God's rebuke for being rude to me.

"Randy!" I said.

He took a deep breath. "I… didn't… There *wasn't* any saddle," he finally confessed.

"That's right," I said, pleased. "I didn't even have a saddle for her, so I rode bareback."

His countenance relaxed. He didn't seem to mind the trick question.

There was no saddle.

That. That impressed me.

I asked Matthew what it's like when he has a vision, and he said:

"Let me think for a second. It's like a memory. Have you ever had a vivid memory? Or a dream when you know it's a dream - have you had those before? Like you're there. Like it's real, but you know that it's not. It's kinda like that. In my mind, it's almost like I'm seeing two different things. Like, I'm looking at what's really in front of me, and I'm looking at a dream in front of me. It seems like I'm in two different places or two different realities and seeing them both simultaneously. But, they're distinct. It's not like they're merging or anything. So, the best I can describe it, it's like a really vivid memory."

Ten years later, about two months before he died, Randy told me about another vision he'd had.

Despite the different injuries he'd had over the years, Randy had been strong and healthy when I'd married him. He could pick up logs and carry them on his shoulders, impressing all the teen boys at summer camp when we were counselors. He worked harder than any two men, and he felt great. He tweaked his back again during a softball game, but he still refused to take a Tylenol for pain.

When we moved back to West Virginia, though, Randy slowly started to deteriorate. Toward the end, he started depending on pain medications again. I found his beer bottles out in the woods where he'd go to drink alone. He was sick and weak and desperate for muscle relaxers. He lived for years in daily agony, and he'd started to just fall apart. He had so little strength left, and I know it weighed on him. He didn't want to live like that for the rest of his life.

He told me, "I asked the Lord, 'What do you have for me? Where is all this going? What is Your purpose for me?' Then, God gave me a vision. He showed me that I was before His throne, worshiping Him. It was all okay. I was His son, and I was accepted."

At the time, I felt insecure because Randy was the one who had visions. Randy was the one who prayed for people and they got healed. God spoke out loud to Randy, and Randy would know about things before they happened. When Elizabeth Smart was kidnapped in 2002, he kept saying, "She's alive. We have to pray for her, because she's alive." He didn't say that about Natalee Holloway or Chandra Levy or any other women who had famously gone missing. Then, Elizabeth Smart was found, having survived those horrific nine months with her captors. Randy was always right.

I didn't have visions. God didn't talk out loud to me. Now, here God was giving my husband a vision of Heaven, and he was there and I wasn't.

"Where was I?" I asked, thinking that somehow I had been left out. Randy got to hang out with God, and I was left behind. How could that be?

"That's not ..." Randy shook his head and tried to explain. "It was just to comfort me," he said. "It was to let me know that He loved me, that I was His, that I was accepted." He felt like he was failing, but God hadn't rejected him.

Randy wanted to live. He'd been through terrible things in his life, and the one thing that God had given him was a real sense of His love. And hope. Randy had hope. Dying young and leaving us behind was not Randy's plan. Looking back, I can see that he was worried he might die. I know he didn't want to.

I've thought about that vision a lot in the years since. A dozen things could have been done differently that day to save Randy's life, but God absolutely let him die in that stupid way. Painlessly. In bed. Asleep. Frankly, I think I'd rather he'd jumped in front of a bus to save a child.

Maybe Randy was the one who had visions, but I know that last vision served as much as a mercy to me as to my husband. It reminded me that Randy's death was okay. It wasn't a terrible mistake. It wasn't my fault for not being there to save him. It wasn't Randy's fault for leaving me. His Heavenly Father had taken him Home, and he was safe. I was still standing out on first base, but he'd made it home, and that was a good thing.

What do you say to Grandma when she isn't healed, and she thinks God doesn't love her? What do we say to hurting people who think God doesn't care?

CHAPTER 26

TECTONICS

At a specified time the earth can have had just one configuration. But the earth supplies no direct information about this. We are like a judge confronted by a defendant who declines to answer, and we must determine the truth from the circumstantial evidence. All the proofs we can muster have the deceptive character of this type of evidence. How would we assess a judge who based his decision on part of the available data only?

It is only by combining the information furnished by all the earth sciences that we can hope to determine "truth" here, that is to say, to find the picture that sets out all the known facts in the best arrangement and that therefore has the highest degree of probability. Further, we have to be prepared always for the possibility that each new discovery, no matter which science furnishes it, may modify the conclusions we draw."

-Alfred Wegener (1928)[1]

Alfred Wegener truly attempted to follow his own words here, and he was laughed at and scorned for the observations he made and the conclusions he drew. But, it turned out he was mostly right.

In 1912, Alfred Wegener presented his idea that the continents were in motion and that the major land masses had once all connected in a massive supercontinent he called Pangea, meaning

---

1   Wegener, A., & Biram, J. (1966). Foreward. In *The Origin of Continents and Oceans* (4th ed.), Dover Publications: New York.)

"all earth." He pointed out that the east coast of South America looked like a puzzle piece that would have once fit snugly against the west coast of Africa. He noted that the fossils of certain plants and animals on both coasts matched one another, which made sense if the lands had once been connected. He realized that the coal seams under Antarctica's ice meant the frozen land once held significant plant life, and he suggested that Antarctica was once situated closer to the equator.

Wegener's ideas about continental drift were ridiculed by the geological community of his day. How could entire land masses move? That was absurd! Wegener didn't have a solid mechanism for his "continental displacement" theory, so the orthodoxy treated him with hostility and insisted that land bridges had allowed animals to cross oceans. They declared there were alternate explanations for the things Wegener had observed, and his ideas were tossed away after his death.

Decades later, Harry Hess discovered the reality of sea floor spreading, and the theory of plate tectonics stepped into respectability. Oops. Sorry Wegener. Our bad. We now know that the continents and ocean floor float as plates on a hot "plastic" asthenosphere. Wegener had the right idea, even if he didn't have a way of ascertaining the mechanism. Today, geologists monitor plate boundaries for earthquakes and volcanic activity, and school children are taught about Pangea as a matter of course.

We squabble about a lot of things as humans. We rumble and scrape against each other like billions of tiny faults creating billions of tiny earthquakes. Sometimes we have good ideas, and sometimes we have just plain nutty ideas that have no basis in reality. Each of us is a tectonic force, whether we build beautiful mountains or destroy each other. In the end, I do believe all our pushing and scraping can get us to the truth. The little rumbles are uncomfortable, but I think the truth eventually rumbles right up to the surface.

CHAPTER 27

THANKS GIVING

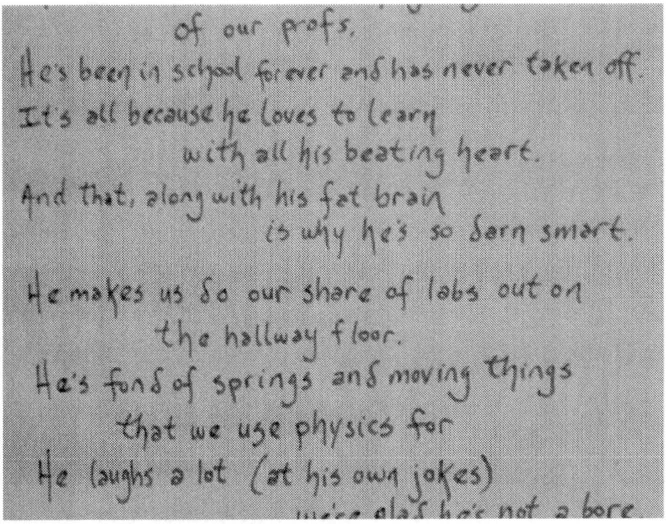

of our profs,
He's been in school forever and has never taken off.
It's all because he loves to learn
with all his beating heart.
And that, along with his fat brain
is why he's so darn smart.
He makes us do our share of labs out on
the hallway floor.
He's fond of springs and moving things
that we use physics for
He laughs a lot (at his own jokes)
we're glad he's not a bore.

Figure 22 - From the poem we placed on Flash's office door.

Amber had to return to Pennsylvania, so I drove her back home over that next weekend. Monday, the Sigma Pi Epsilon chemistry fraternity members gathered for the wild and crazy job of writing thank you notes to our professors. We gathered around the table in the Cheminar Room, busily jotting out notes. We were free the whole next week for Thanksgiving.

"Who wants Dr. Vallo and Dr. Park!" Sigma Pi Epsilon President Furby asked. Several of us volunteered, attaching our notes to little bags filled with KitKats and Reese's peanut butter cups.

We didn't hit just the chemistry professors with love. We gifted every science prof in the building.

Dr. Zenith received a note and yummy goodies just like everybody else, and we heard about it Wednesday in class. Did he say, "Hey, that was nice!" No, he did not.

"The chemistry fraternity has given me a note along with this bag of chocolate." He held up the offending gift. "Okay. If I'm poisoned by these and die, you guys have to do two things. First, honor my dead body. Next, go enact vengeance on Sigma Pi Epsilon."

Moral: Be careful about little gestures of kindness toward Dr. Zenith.

Well, it was too late, because Matthew and I had already gathered gifts for the First-Floor professors on behalf of all their students. I'd already written poems of honor for each professor. I'd collected sheets of rich brown paper from Zeke's preschool teacher, and I'd carefully written out the words Wednesday night while the children bounced around like pistons. I'd done some interviewing for Dr. Gurden and Dr. Wasser's poems in order to properly represent them, and we'd filled baskets with crossword puzzles and flavored coffees and DVDs and other fun stuff. We gave Dr. Wasser the movie *Lady In The Water*, because he was the water science professor. Dr. Stillwell got *Dirty Rotten Scoundrels* because he's Dr. Stillwell. Late Wednesday night, I posted the poems to the outside of the professors' doors, and early Thursday morning Matthew delivered the Thanksgiving baskets filled with goodies.

And we heard about it in our physics lab that afternoon.

"By the way," Dr. Zenith opened up at the beginning of class. "If you were involved in giving me the basket, thank you. It was awesome. If you weren't involved, I got a basket with a bunch of cool stuff including a superhero book and *chocolate*. And I got a poem too. It was also awesome. So, thank you."

No threats. No violence planned or suspicions held. No. He thought it was awesome. Yes! Dr. Zenith taped his poem up on the wall next to his desk, readily visible from the door. Flash taped up his poem on the back of his door, so he could read it from his desk when his door was closed. Both poems hang in their offices to this day.

Flash left a rhyming thank you note for us on his door. I thought that was great.

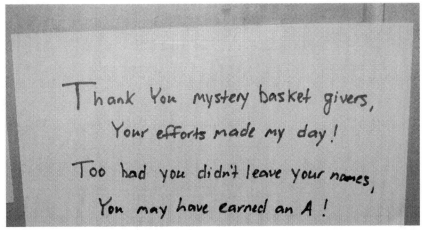

Figure 23 - Flash in poet mode.

On the other hand, Dr. Stillwell's basket sat outside his door all morning. He was gone to Charleston that day, and somebody moved his basket for him. He didn't say anything about it when he came back. And he didn't enjoy its contents either. His basket sat on the back counter of his office for two years, and I eventually ate all his chocolate, drank all his flavored coffees, and took *Dirty Rotten Scoundrels* home to watch.

CHAPTER 28

KNOWING GOD'S LOVE

From the age of five, I was out exploring the woods with my friend Laura. We crossed ravines on logs and tried to keep from getting our shoes stuck in the mud at the pond. We lost Laura's brand new winter coat one time, and her mother marched us through the woods that afternoon in search of it. It was lost forever, and Laura and I have cringed and giggled about it in more recent years. We had a lot of fun in those woods, and we'd be gone until dinnertime. My mom had a bevy of younger children to worry about, and I did pretty much whatever I wanted.

"I remember disobeying my mother on two distinct occasions as a child," I'd told Dr. Stillwell and Flash as we climbed up to Seneca Rocks that September.

I felt tension pulse up in the professors, but I just smiled inside. "On the first occasion, I was brought home in a police car, and on the second I broke my hand," I finished. "At that point, I decided it was wise for me to obey my mother."

I have always felt like God raised me from that time onward.

Mom and Dad separated when I was seven. Mom eventually remarried, but I never got close to my stepfather. He ran up huge debts and then skipped town when I was 12, leaving my mother a pregnant, depressed mess.[1] After little Max was born, Mom stayed home with the baby during the day and then went off most evenings to make money. She had to leave me to watch four little kids and an infant, because childcare was just too expensive.

---

1   I hear what you're thinking - you know who you are - and you can just back up a little bit there. My mother produces amazing children who are an asset to this world. We should all be grateful that her efforts at birth control failed repeatedly.

Mom helped me study for spelling bees and offered words of wisdom now and then, but she dropped most of the whole mother-role thing during those years. She became this bizarre anti-parent, keeping me up to watch *The Tonight Show* with her. The summer my stepdad left, she made me play cards late into the night. "Mom, the birds are chirping," I'd say, and she'd finally agree to go to bed. I think she had entered an emotional black cloud and didn't want to lay awake thinking all night. Instead, she forced me to keep her company until exhaustion won over.

She told me to go to bed once when I was a teenager, and I gave her a confused look. "What?"

"I tell you to go to bed!" she insisted.

"Mom," I reminded her, "you're the one telling me, 'Honey, wake up. It's your turn to draw a card.'"

She didn't turn to alcohol or drugs or prostitution, and we laughed a lot together. She was just depressed. I had my own burdens as a teenager, but I couldn't share my griefs with her. She had too many of her own.

I didn't cause any problems. I did well in school and I stayed out of trouble. I enjoyed the fact that Mom treated me like an adult. I helped take care of the house and other kids as well as a 13-year-old can.

I try to think of other girls my age watching five wild children all the time. Baby Max never stopped crying. The nine-year-old twins fought constantly with Heather and Whitney. Heather would purposely provoke the boys, and Shadow would grab whatever weapon was handy and chase the girls through the house, roaring from his healthy lungs. I'd have to step in - dodge - dance - grab the fire poker or hammer or whatever from Shadow's fist and wrestle him into a closet. Then before Shadow escaped, I'd wrap my arms around Heather and heave her outside to remove her from the situation. That was a typical afternoon.

We had pleasant times too. We rode our bikes everywhere around the Spokane Valley. I learned to bake, because the food we got from the food bank consisted primarily of staples like cornmeal and flour and sugar and salt and eggs. Baron and Shadow and I liked to sit on the roof under the stars and drink our delicious and comforting hot corn meal mush from mugs. It was nice.

I told Dr. Stillwell one afternoon, "When I was 12, I'd get up in the middle of the night, and I'd ride my bike five miles down to the Mica Hills. I never asked my mother, and I don't think she even knows. But, I'd climb up through the trees and sit and wait quietly for deer or other animals to walk by. I never saw anything but a screech owl, but I'd still get to watch the sunrise."

Dr. Stillwell's eyes smiled when I told him that.

Nobody screamed at me and called me names. Nobody beat me up or raped me. Nobody interrogated me about where I had been all day. I just had to take care of myself.

Mom tried. She wanted me to get a good education, so she sent me to a Jesuit high school in Spokane where all my fellow students' parents were bankers and lawyers and city officials. Meanwhile, I did my homework amidst bellowing children while we lost our house because of the mess my stepfather left behind. Mom eventually recovered, but it took some years.

I bathed every day. I took the money I earned from babysitting and rode my bike down to the thrift store to buy myself clothes. I organized the kids and we'd de-chaos the house once in awhile. We ate. We stayed warm. We didn't kill each other.

I didn't know how to buy a bra though. I remember going to school, trying to hide my developing body under layers of baggy shirts.

I broke my thumb playing soccer my freshman year of high school, and nobody took me to the doctor. Some hormonal boys tried to get too friendly with me on the bus, and I told them to get lost. They punished me for it in P.E. by smashing into me on the soccer field, and one particular day I hit the ground and broke my right thumb. That knuckle bulges to this day, and I can't extend it as far as the other. It needed medical attention, but I didn't even tell my mother about it. "Hey mom. I broke my thumb. I need X-rays. I need a cast." I don't think I even said that. It just healed on its own ...all defective.

I had to take care of myself, but I was just a kid and I didn't know enough.

I don't remember a time before I loved God. I just know that I've known Him since I was a tiny little kid. It didn't matter whether sermons were bearable. It didn't even matter whether people were kind to me or not. Some of the harshest people in my life have been religious. It didn't matter that my parents divorced, that they made good or bad decisions, that life got chaotic. It didn't matter if I was miserable and lonely - because I was. My faith in God did not depend on any of those things, because I lived in His presence. I knew God myself. He taught me and moved in me and showed me things. He filled my insides. He directed me and He did miracles in my life. He's real, and I know it. And sometimes I've been stuck with it, whether I liked it or not.

And when I say, "I know God," what I mean is that I know God the way a little kid knows her father. The small child doesn't know about all the big important things the father is doing at work. The child doesn't know about the bills that have to be paid or the problems with electricity or plumbing in the house. The little kid only knows what her father is like, whether he's stern or kind, safe or cruel, gentle or violent. I know what God is like. I know how He treats *me*.

In the end, I always felt that God Himself took hold of me. He trained me and showed me how to follow Him, how to trust Him. He did not give me secret knowledge about doctrinal issues. I don't know what the wheels with eyes in Ezekiel are all about. I don't know whether Jesus will return in my lifetime. I don't know. But, He's shown me simpler, more personal things.

For instance, He helped me to know that He loved me. I mean, I believed it in my head, but I had a hard time *knowing* He loved me. Feeling it. Trusting it. He had to help me get there, and He didn't do it all at once. He built it in me brick by brick. He formed my faith slowly, solidly. He forced my spiritual roots to dig down deep deep to find water, because that made me strong. He didn't give His presence to me easily; I had to hunger for Him, to seek Him and want Him. He developed our relationship so that when the winds blew hard, I didn't get knocked over. When Randy died, I still felt solid. Randy wasn't in pain anymore, and that was a mercy for him. He was safe. He was okay. I felt relieved for him.

The most important thing God has shown me over the years, though, is the importance of trusting in His love. He wants me to depend on it. I'm so silly. He'll direct me to do something I don't want to do, and I reactively feel He's just being mean to me. But, if I obey Him anyway, I see how smart it was after all. It's like, "See! I only want good for you, Amy Joy! Just trust me next time!"

I found that when I did trust God, when I had confidence in His love for me, He gave me anything I asked for. Even little things. "Boy, I could use some chicken nuggets," I might think. Ten seconds later: "Hey Amy, you want the rest of my chicken nuggets?" Even silly things. The trouble was never with God, as though He only loved me now and then. The trouble was that it took me a long time to have confidence in His love. I haven't often been able to totally rest and wallow in it. I've gotten better at it, but it's taken a lot of years. It's hard to live confidently in God's protection and provision when you spend your childhood feeling exceptionally unimportant.

Once I learned to trust in His love, though, He'd do anything. Anything.

So, what about Grandma? What about her? What do you say to her when she doesn't get healed?

You remind her of the truth. You say, "Grandma, God does love you. He loves you so much. Maybe He will still heal you, and maybe He won't. But, no matter what He does, you are absolutely valuable to Him, and it's okay. Trust Him, Grandma. You are precious to Him, and He'll take care of everything." Above all else, that's what God taught me, and that's what I'd pass on to dear Grandma.

Because God will do anything. He'll heal people. He'll split mountains. He'll calm fires. He will do absolutely anything.

CHAPTER 29

THE FIRE BURNS

A fire started in our basement when I was three-years-old, and my parents left me and newborn baby Heather upstairs while they tried to put it out. "Watch Heather," they told me. "Make sure she's okay."

Heather wasn't going anywhere on my parents' water bed. She couldn't even roll over yet. I kneeled there on the red shag carpet and pretended to comfort her.

"It's okay, Heather," I said. "Don't worry. It's a big fire, Heather. It's a really big fire."

I wanted it to be a really big fire, because that was exciting. Mom and Dad had been talking, and I knew that if the fire got out of control, they were going to send me down the street to stay with the neighbors. In the middle of the night!

In the end, the firemen arrived and I was walked down the block where they gave me Big Bird slippers in honor of the occasion. Fantastic evening in the life of a three-year-old!

I don't know how the fire started that night or how much damage it did. We didn't have to move out of our house. My mom says that when the flames burned through the phone line, it made the phone ring once.

One ring. That was important.

Half a year later, we flew on an airplane (right through the clouds!) to visit the Dowd family with their six kids in Arvada, Colorado. Dad had to stay back home and work, but Mom and Lex and Heather and I were on vacation! I knew my fourth birthday was coming up, and every day I asked, "Is it my birthday today? Is it my birthday today?" It's hard being little and having no concept of dates and calendars. It's hard being little and having short legs, and when your big brother says, "I'll race you to that telephone pole!" he always always wins. So unfair.

Lex and I slept in a twin bed downstairs in the basement, down where Jimmy and Mikey Dowd had their bunk bed. The laundry room and Mr. Dowd's office were also down there. Everybody else slept two stories farther up, above the main floor of the big house. All except Mom, who was staying on the couch in the living room.

The fourth of July came, and Mom explains that Mr. Dowd wouldn't let her go to sleep that night; he wanted to stay up and finish his show while she waited patiently for her couch to free up. Tired. Tired. Late on the fourth of July. The kids all asleep. Waiting waiting. Tired.

Then the phone rang. Just once. Mom got up to go answer it, and as she did, she passed by the basement stairs.

Mrs. Dowd said, "Do you smell smoke?"

Mom's mind flashed back to that night half a year earlier when the fire burned through our phone line. She opened the door to the basement, and thick, choking smoke billowed out of the basement at her. She could see flames down below, under the stairs.

I remember that night. I remember Lex shaking me awake. I am sure Mom was there too, but in my memory I can only see Lex.

"Wake up, Amy," he pulled me up. "Wake up!"

I looked around the room through the hazy smoke. We were low enough in our little bed that we hadn't breathed in too much, but the boys in the bunk bed didn't want to wake up at all.

"Get up you guys!" we told them. "There's a fire! We have to get out!"

Mr. Dowd appeared and started dragging kids out of the room.

I don't remember how I got out of the basement. The next scene in my head is of Mrs. Dowd with a baby in her arms, stepping down the stairs from the top floor. Mom opened the basement door a last time thinking she would grab some clothes, but it was too late; the flames were chewing up the stairs. We all hustled outside, and the firemen came.

Minutes. That's all we'd had.

If Mr. Dowd hadn't wanted to finish his show… If we hadn't had that other fire and the phone hadn't rung once…Who pays attention to a single phone ring? It's always just somebody changing his mind, saying, "Oh, it's too late there. I shouldn't be calling now from Hong Kong." Even smelling smoke, they might not have gone hunting for a fire. It was July fourth, when the streets are filled with smoke from people shooting off fireworks. The adults would have gone to bed. Lex and I and the boys would have died first. We were in the basement, right there next to the laundry room where a hat had fallen down behind a faulty hot water heater.

We spent the rest of our vacation with the Dowds in a motel. For my birthday I got an inflatable tiger floatie, which I used to swim in the motel pool. Mom had to use peanut butter to work a chunk of bubble gum out of my hair. I got into trouble for jumping on the bed, which was so unfair because five-year-old Teresa Dowd had been jumping freely a few minutes before.

At least Lex didn't let Teresa beat me when she wanted to race.

Which all leads to November, 2010, when I started a fire in my backyard at the cabin.

Randy and I had a burn pile out back we used to destroy credit card applications and bills and statements we didn't particularly want going into the common trash. The pile had grown large that autumn, because it included not just my paper garbage, but the scrap wood and old subflooring and construction burnables that Gary had thrown there while remodeling the house. I had a nice big pile to burn that Saturday, November 27th. A bonfire.

I poured a little fuel on it, set it on fire and watched the flames grow.

The burn pile was in a small clearing right next to the woods. A very small clearing. I watched the flames climb and the fire spread, growing bigger as the heat hit all that dry wood. As it rose into the air, I realized with horror that the wind was blowing. I hadn't even been paying attention.

"I am such an idiot!" I shouted, watching in dismay as the wind blew those full-sized flames right toward the woods - woods full of oak trees that had just lost their dry brown leaves - leaves piled in a thick new, combustible layer.

"I'm so stupid!" I said again. "I lit a fire when the wind is blowing! Randy would never have lit a fire when the wind was blowing!" I looked around and tried to think how to calm it. The fire was already getting big, and I didn't even have an outside spigot to hook a hose to.

"Please calm the fire down," I began to beg God. "Please calm the fire. Please calm the fire."

No change. No improvement at all. The wind picked up, and little flaming pieces of paper fluttered into the trees. I already knew how easily those leaves caught fire. We were in serious danger - I had just burned up my property and my neighbors houses. I had just ruined lives. It hadn't happened yet, but I'd started the chain of events. I was such an idiot!

"Please calm down the fire!" I begged. "Please calm the fire!" I felt hopeless. God wasn't listening. The fire was really crackling now, and the wind kept blowing the flames right toward the dry brush and piles of loose, dry leaves.

"Wait a minute," I thought. "Wait. I'm praying wrong. I'm praying in fear, as though God doesn't even care." I took a deep breath. "I'm praying as though God doesn't love me. And He does. He loves me."

I had spent many years expecting the worst, expecting destruction and tragedy. I had gotten so used to it - and used to trusting God to carry me through it - that I hadn't learned to expect salvation from Him. I didn't expect Him to actually rescue me from tragedy itself. Here, though. Here I had a new thought.

"God doesn't want my woods to burn down," I realized. "He loves me. He loves my neighbors. He doesn't want me to burn down their houses!" It was a new perspective - that He actually didn't want bad things happening in my life all the time. He was willing to save and protect me. "Jesus loves me," I told myself. "Jesus loves me. Jesus loves me. Jesus loves me." I said it over and over until my spirit calmed down and I wasn't afraid anymore.

Then, when I had confidence that God loved me, that He wanted to rescue me, I said to the healthy, roaring fire, "In Jesus' name, calm down."

And Whoosh.

It's hard to describe. The fire just whoomped. It emptied or shrunk. It just insta-calmed. It wasn't like the wind simply died. The fire did a physical thing where it puffed out the sides, as though a giant invisible blanket were thrown over it. It acted like it suddenly didn't have enough oxygen. One moment the flames were all big and orange and noisy as the wind gushed through them, and the next moment the big flames were gone and the fire burned with a low blue flame. There was plenty of wood left - plenty of fuel - but I suddenly had a large blue campfire in my yard and not a county hazard.

I stared in astonishment for a few seconds, and then I shouted, "WOW! Let's try that *again*!"

It was the most amazing thing. I had never seen anything like it, like... super miracle... right in front of my face.

I guarded the fire until it burned down to nothing. A bit later the wind picked up, but I didn't have to worry because it didn't have much effect. In the end, I hauled out water to throw on it.

That was the relieving end to my Thanksgiving break.

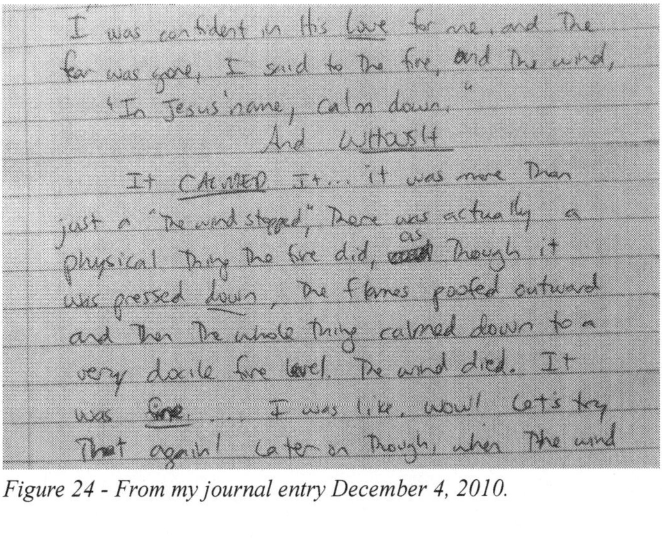
I was confident in His Love for me, and The fear was gone, I said to The fire, and The wind, "In Jesus' name, calm down."

And WHOOSH

It CALMED. It... it was more Than just a "The wind stopped," There was actually a physical Thing The fire did, as Though it was pressed down, The flames poofed outward and Then The whole Thing calmed down to a very docile fire level. The wind died. It was fine... I was like, wow! Let's try That again! Later on Though, when The wind

Figure 24 - From my journal entry December 4, 2010.

CHAPTER 30

FINAL EXAMS

You'd think I'd go back to school and grab Dr. Derlidger by the shoulders and bellow, "I told a fire to calm in Jesus' name and it CALMED!!" You'd think I'd do that, that I'd badger every person I met with the wild news. But, I didn't.

I told Matthew, of course. I'm sure I called my brother Baron and my parents, but it's not one of those things that easily opens a discussion in Cell Biology. Who would believe me?

Writing these things has improved my view of history. It has given familiar stories new life. When I think of Abraham Lincoln at Ford's Theater, I can see him settling down in the quiet sanctuary of his booth. I can see him feeling in his pockets for his spectacles to read the playbill, pulling out his watch and checking the time, leaning over to whisper a joke to his wife. I see Moses stepping out the door of his tent to spit the grit out of his teeth. I see him settling back down inside to write about the recent snake attack and the healings that followed, feeling weary to his bones of living with multitudes of grouchy, complaining people.

The conversations and events in this book really happened to me, and I don't realize until I read them back to myself how they sound like tales you'd find on somebody else's bookshelf...if that makes sense. Yet, because my stories are true, it's easier to believe that other people's stories are true in a more tangible, sore feet and sweat and hot-sun-headache sort of way.

The Fire Episode opened up a whole new vista in my faith life. I felt like a barrier had fallen away, as though the plywood of the visible world blocked our view of the whole Reality and I had glimpsed that free new world through a hole in the wall. Any one of us could reach out and grab the finger of God like little children, and He could crack mountains in half for us. Maybe He even wanted to. Maybe that would delight His heart.

The Hebrew children stood in a furnace and weren't burned. Elijah called down fire from Heaven to burn up his sacrifice after the prophets of Baal failed. Sennacherib's army was decimated at Jerusalem, and they pulled out without conquering the city. These are not isolated incidents.

I did tell Dr. Derlidger and Dr. Manchester about the fire the next semester, but I never bothered most people. Maybe I should have, but I didn't. Even when I told Dr. Derlidger, he just dismissed it. Killing a fire in Jesus' name just didn't fit into his paradigm of reality. He offered suggestions like, "Maybe the wind died." He didn't call me a liar or accuse me of being nuts. He just shrugged it off.

Anyway. The end of that semester drew near, and nobody had time for casual conversations. I had to finish the killer lab notebook for Dr. Vallo's Organic Chemistry class and a heavy take-home test for the Lidge. We had ridiculous numbers of reactions and theorems and rules and equations and complex biochemical processes to remember for our upcoming exams. Insanity.

The transmission went out on Randy's old truck, leaving me stranded on Route 901 on the way to school one morning. My stepson's friends had broken out the truck's back window and driven around while the transmission fluid leaked out. They brought it back, but the transmission was shot. That was a spectacular Monday.

I hardly got to talk to Dr. Stillwell at all. The end of his semester proved as busy as the end of mine, and we had no time for merry conversations. Even a brief laugh he gave after class one day seemed forced and joyless.

I stopped by his office the Wednesday after Thanksgiving Break, glad to visit him for a moment, discouraged and heart-sad that I had seen so little of him.

"How are you doing, Amy Joy?" the good doctor asked.

Skepticism at his sincerity flushed over me. "Do you really care? Does it really matter to you?" I asked. I didn't mean it rudely. I just didn't want anything false from him. No forced laughter or polite facades or empty niceties.

The pitch of his voice raised a bit. "Of course it does!" Dr. S. said. "I worry about you."

I wanted to tell him about the real things that were affecting me, things beyond lice or people breaking into my workshop. The things that rocked me most were my need for a caring mentor and the fullness of my spiritual life. Those two things drilled through my mantle deep into the core of my being, exposing layers that could never be touched by exams, oak floors, skinned knuckles and broken trucks.

And poor Dr. Stillwell, dear man, was at the center of my distractions in both of those areas.

CHAPTER 31

CATHEDRALS

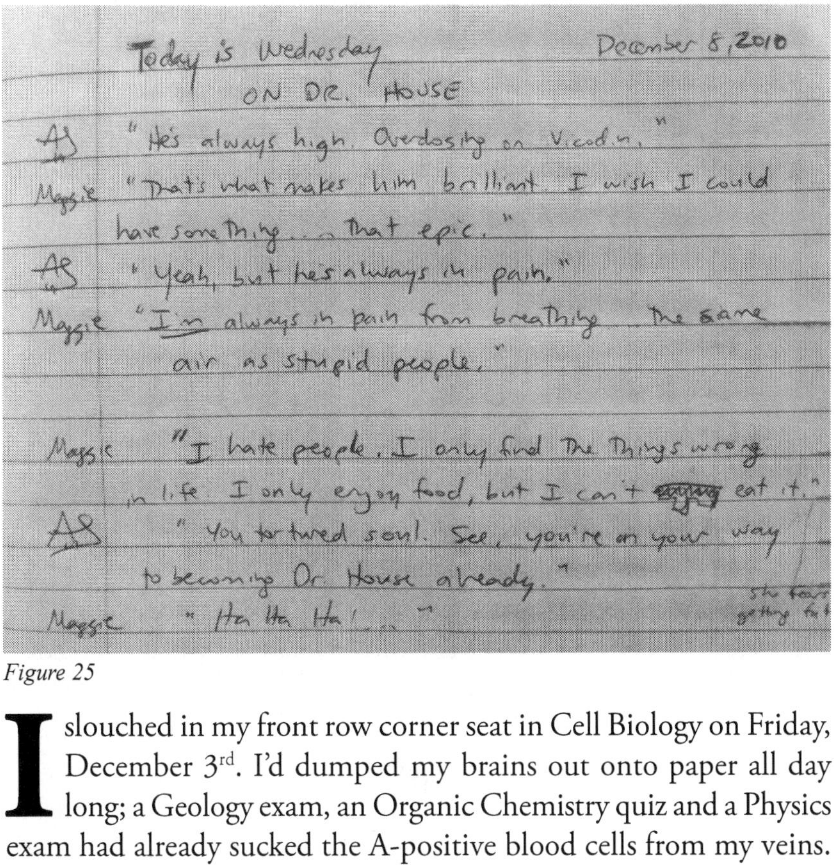

Today is Wednesday   December 8, 2010
          ON DR. HOUSE
AS   "He's always high. Overdosing on Vicodin."
Maggie "That's what makes him brilliant. I wish I could
          have something ... that epic."
AS   "Yeah, but he's always in pain."
Maggie "I'm always in pain from breathing the same
          air as stupid people."

Maggie "I hate people. I only find the things wrong
          in life. I only enjoy food, but I can't ~~enjoy~~ eat it."
AS   "You tortured soul. See, you're on your way
          to becoming Dr. House already."
Maggie "Ha Ha Ha!..."
                                                    she fears
                                                    getting fat

Figure 25

I slouched in my front row corner seat in Cell Biology on Friday, December 3rd. I'd dumped my brains out onto paper all day long; a Geology exam, an Organic Chemistry quiz and a Physics exam had already sucked the A-positive blood cells from my veins. My body crumpled in a little pile in my front row seat as I finished up my final Cell quiz. I slouched there, waiting for Dr. Derlidger's lecture to start, his last hurrah before finals week.

The Lidge gazed down at me. "Oh," he apologized. "Am I keeping you awake?"

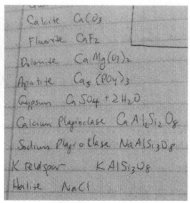

Figure 26 - Above: Hybridization of atomic orbitals. Right: Chemical formulas of common geologic minerals.

"Not for long," I answered.

He laughed out loud and said, "Clever."

Honestly, I shook from exhaustion. I held out my hand and watched it tremble. The semester hadn't conquered me, but it had put up a brutal offensive.

Friday, December 10th, Dr. Stillwell handed us lecture and lab finals in Physical Geology. He tossed in essay questions on subjects we'd barely touched in class.

"It was in the book," Dr. Stillwell said callously.

Essay questions! That man is not fully sane!

So, of course it took me longer than anybody else to finish, and Dr. Stillwell let me stay late. I wearily handed him my bundle of papers and headed toward the hall. He followed me, turning off the lights and locking the door behind us.

Then Dr. S. said something to me. I don't remember what it was exactly. He didn't say, "Well, you have a nice Christmas, Amy Joy." He didn't say that. He didn't say, "Boy, I'm glad this semester is over. It's been a rough one." No, as he closed the lab door, he said something nasty about religious people.

Was that necessary? In what could have been our last moment of camaraderie for the semester, Dr. S. chose to make a snide remark about religious something or another.

Seven months earlier, I'd been warned not to argue with the good doctor. I'd been told to be quiet in September when I'd wanted to wrestle over geological issues. I'd longed to explain to Dr. Stillwell the things God had been doing all semester, and time and again I'd been stymied. Now, with that last harsh comment of his, I'd been given the freedom to talk.

"You've just been inoculated," I said to him. "You've been given a dead version of a real thing." He'd been brought up in a religious household, but there had been no life, no joy in it. He'd been shown the statue rather than the living Lord. We turned and started to walk down the hall. "Do you know," I challenged him, "I've had more miracles happen in my life than any 10 people?"

"Oh *really*," he answered.

Dr. Stillwell was my geology professor. He did not sit over coffee with me talking about how neat God was. I had told him about the fire that split and avoided old Mr. Davies' house, but that was it. I hadn't told him about any miracles in my own life.

I said, "Just two weeks ago - at the end of Thanksgiving Break - I started a fire in my back yard. You know, a trash pile fire. I had credit card statements and things I didn't want to go into the general garbage. All kinds of papers, plus construction trash and the old wood Gary tore out of my house. I piled it all up, and I set it on fire. Then, as the flames grew, I realized that the wind was blowing. 'I'm such an idiot!' I told myself. 'Randy would never have started a fire when the wind was blowing!' The burn pile is right near the woods where all the dry leaves and brush are two feet deep."

I left nothing out as we walked down to his office.

"'Please calm the fire, Lord. Please calm the fire.' I begged. Nothing changed. Bits of burning paper were blowing into the woods," I grinned at the doctor as we reached his office door. "'PLEASE calm the fire. Please!'

"Then I realized I was praying wrong. All the times in my life when God has really answered my prayers, it's when I had confidence He loved me. I… I have to figure out a lot of these things myself…"

I looked up at Dr. Stillwell and he nodded.

"So I started reminding myself, 'Jesus loves me. Jesus loves me…'"

I finished the story there at his office door. I told him I commanded that fire to calm in Jesus' name, and it instantly died down.

"It poofed out to the sides!" I said. "It was like a giant blanket was thrown on it. And the flames went all calm and blue."

Dr. Stillwell pulled out his keys and opened his door. "But see," he said. "I wasn't there." He walked into his office and I followed him in.

Did I really expect my story to change Dr. Stillwell's mind? His heart? Did I expect him to be amazed? Not really. I expected him to be skeptical, because I would have been skeptical myself if somebody had told me that story. I would have asked questions, though. I would have tried to get to the bottom of it. I expected skepticism, but I didn't expect that hard, cold response from the geologist. It ticked me off.

Dr. Stillwell knew me. He knew me well enough by that point to know that if I told him something, he could believe it. He had no cause for disbelief based on *me*. His causes were internal to himself. He had a bias, and he chose his bias contrary to his knowledge of my personality, contrary to his firsthand knowledge of my intellectual honesty and my intolerance for anything fake.

He chose not to believe me, because he simply didn't want to.

"Look," I leaned on his big wooden desk and stared into his face, feeling hostile. "I don't give a sh-- if you believe the same things I do. But, I want you to be able to make decisions based on sufficient data."

Dr. Stillwell met my eyes and nodded. "That's a good attitude to have."

It didn't matter. He wasn't going to accept that I had just witnessed a miracle.

I plopped down into my cushioned seat, frustrated at him. What was his problem!

"What is your deal then?" I asked him.

He took a moment and gazed at me across the desk. "I have been in some of the most beautiful cathedrals in the world," he said evenly. "I've been in the Vatican and... just some of the most beautiful cathedrals, and I've found that nature is better than any church. I love going out hiking like we did. But most of the wars in the world have been caused by religion, and I think that if God were real, He'd be an atheist."

I couldn't disagree with him about the cathedrals. The day of our hike up to Seneca Rocks, I'd sneaked away early in the morning before anybody else awoke. I'd picked my way through the woods, past smooth trunks spotted by mosses and up onto a mound of granite rising above the soft forest floor. There, I'd gazed straight up through the young oaks and watched scattered bits of morning mist blow across the treetops, so close I felt I could hear them whisper. The water vapor streamed past, like a parade just above my head, and the sun glowed pink and golden through the wisps like a glimpse of glory. There I'd sung to my Creator who'd thought it all up.

"Your love, oh Lord, reaches to the heavens. Your faithfulness stretches to the skies. Your righteousness is like the mighty mountains, and your justice flows like the ocean tides. And I will lift my voice to worship you my King, and I will find my strength in the shadow of your wings."[1]

I can't believe all our form and show, our kneel-stand-kneel-stand rituals impress God any more than they do Dr. Stillwell. We are the temples of the Holy Spirit. The heavens declare the glory of God.

In a way, I think Dr. Stillwell is right. I think God is against the form of religion without the life of His Spirit. He's against focusing on the rules without getting close *to Him*. "He'd be anti-religion," I suggested to Dr. Stillwell. "He wouldn't be an atheist."

At the same time, Dr. Stillwell needed to know there was spiritual substance to be had past the wooden pews and candles. "God has been with me all my life," I told him. "I really consider Him to be the one that raised me. For so much of my life it was just Him and me."

Dr. Stillwell dismissed me again. "You needed somebody," he said, not unkindly. He thought I'd invented a relationship with an invisible friend so I wouldn't have to be alone.

"I told a fire to calm, and it did," I countered.

He just brushed it aside. "Your experiences are one thing. But they're subjective. But for me, I didn't experience them."

---

1   This is a Third Day song borrowed from Psalm 36:5-7.

His voice was like a brick wall when he said it.

I have had the opportunity to tell Dr. Stillwell about a number of other miracles in the months and years since that December day, of other moments in my life when God has tapped my shoulder. It's gotten to where I'll be telling a story and I'll stop and say, "Is it okay if I tell the God part of this story?" and Dr. Stillwell always nods. Aside from his gentle response to Mr. Davies and the wildfire, Dr. Stillwell has never once tried to investigate. He has never asked me more questions, working to get to the core of the issue. Invariably, he has spouted some preconceived empty idea that doesn't begin to answer the breadth of the matter.

Dr. Stillwell believes that I invented a relationship with God because I was a lonely child, that I was psychologically damaged, that I have an amazing imagination, that I've interpreted events as "God" because my family raised me on Him.

The thing he says that just annoys me is, "Well. It works for you."

He's not being rude at all when he says it. He's trying to let me have my faith and my experience and just let it go. But, I'm irritated with him because it's a cop out. He just plain doesn't care about figuring out the real answer to the question. He likes his comfort zone.

How can a scientist say, "It works for you," as though that answers anything? I'm not in some other universe, my own little special universe where the rules are completely different. I live in the same world he does. There's a reason it "works" for me, and he's never bothered to ask the questions to get to the bottom of it.

Matthew's dad the clinical psychologist assures me that I'm psychologically healthy, by the way. I think it's providential that he's in my life, just so that he can verify my sanity to the world. He told me one day, "You have some issues, Amy Joy, but you're pretty stable. On the other hand, Dr. Stillwell needs several years of psychotherapy." I'll admit to you… that charmed me immensely.

Dr. Stillwell is a good teacher and my dear friend, but Toby was right. There's something dangerous inside Dr. Stillwell that appears now and then, and I think he'd be better off if he were freed from it.

I'm sure things have happened in Dr. Stillwell's life, things that have deeply discouraged him, and I know they're not my business. God has constantly stood between me and the geology professor. He has protected Dr. Stillwell from me, telling me to respect him and letting me know He loves him. The good doctor's anger and hardness are probably justified. I don't even doubt it. In whatever ways he's been damaged, I still hate it that he just dismisses me. I hate it, especially since he's seen evidence of God's reality in my life himself.

"You have a nice faith," Dr. Stillwell said to me the next summer. "If I thought it would harm you, I would be more opposed to it. But, it's a very nice faith."

"It absolutely would harm me if it weren't true," I responded. "What good is it to reach out to a God who isn't there? If I put all my trust in Him and He doesn't even exist, then I'm going to fall hard. I don't want to believe in a God who isn't there."

Do I have a good imagination? Yes. Was I a lonely child? Yes. Do I have a family that believes in God? Yes. But, I get to tell you this story about Dr. Stillwell because he exists. I didn't invent Dr. Stillwell. I was lonely and needed a father-mentor-friend, but I get to tell you about Dr. Stillwell because it just happens that he's a real guy. I get to tell you about what God is doing in my life because He exists as well. And if He didn't exist, then there would be no good reason for me to believe in Him.

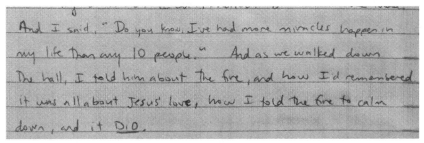

And I said, "Do you know, I've had more miracles happen in my life than any 10 people." And as we walked down the hall, I told him about the fire, and how I'd remembered it was all about Jesus' love, how I told the fire to calm down, and it DID.

Figure 27 - From my journal entry, December 11, 2010.

CHAPTER 32

MERRY CHRISTMAS

O ne more important conversation was had at the end of that year. One more important one. With Kathy Vallo, the wife of my Organic Chemistry professor.

I've mentioned that Dr. and Mrs. Vallo are Hungarian. Dr. Vallo often chatted on the phone in his native tongue, to the delight of the chemistry students. He walked around in his white lab coat, his gray beard neatly trimmed on his chin and his gray hair mostly absent from the top of his head.

Dr. Vallo lived a few blocks down from the university, and it was rumored that he paid students to mow his lawn and rake his leaves. Early during that Fall 2010 semester, I'd jotted at the top of a homework assignment, "Do you need any yard work done?" He stopped me after the next class and said, "I do have some things you could do."

For the rest of my school career, I made a few dollars now and then doing chores for Dr. Vallo. I raked his leaves and cleaned his gutters. I mowed his lawn and swept out his basement. He had me do work for his wonderfully ancient mother in her farmhouse outside of town. My children played in the leaves while I raked them outside. I loved visiting Ildiko. She always invited me in for tea, and when she went to write me a check, she'd pay me for the time I visited with her.

"But, I wasn't working," I protested. "I was having tea with you."

"Oh don't be ridiculous!" she grimaced, and she penned out her generous check.

Ildiko would get up to walk across the kitchen and say, "It takes 100 years what once took five minutes," in her rich Hungarian accent. "When you do work, you do it! You do not just mess around, and zat is so rare zese days."

Dr. Vallo's wife Kathy took advantage of my time too. I helped by mopping and waxing her hardwood floors or vacuuming her upstairs. Dr. Vallo's English is excellent and one has to listen closely to discern his accent. Kathy's accent is stronger, and she often pauses when she talks. I think it's because she has to translate her thoughts from Hungarian into English. We once had a conversation in French, and her French flowed out smoothly, while I was the one pausing to think of how to say what I wanted.

And so the fall semester had ended. With Christmas just two days away, I went to help Kathy Vallo clean her house in preparation for the holiday and visiting family. The Vallo tradition was to put up the tree and decorate it together on Christmas Eve. We dusted and vacuumed and swept and mopped and made the place smell like Pledge and Murphy's Oil.

After the floors were done, I attacked her downstairs bathroom. I kneeled in the tub, scouring, when dear Kathy joined me to chat. While I worked, we began to talk about Christmas and God and Jesus. Then she told me a story that delighted me.

"We were living in a house I just did not like," Kathy began. "I didn't like it. And I was very unhappy. This was many years ago."

"Did you live in this town?" I scrubbed away in her bathtub.

"Yes, Gene was teaching at the college. But, I was not happy. And there came a priest, a visiting priest who had the gift to heal people. So, I went to Mass, and I thought, you know, I thought he would be giving Communion. He had people come up to him, and I thought he was giving Communion. So, I got ready to take Communion, but when I reached him, he put his hand on me and blessed me. And I was... my legs had no strength, and I fell down to the floor. All the way to the floor. But it was not bad. It was good. I felt so much joy and so much happiness inside me and it filled me all the way up to the top of my - of my body. And I felt that God loves me very much. Very much. And when I got up and when I went home it stayed with me. I was so happy. And yes. It is good. Jesus loves us."

I looked up from the tub, my hands dripping suds, and I saw Kathy's eyes full of light as she told the story.

"So, then I went home, and that was the day that Gene said, 'I have found a house I think you will like.' So, we went and looked at it, and it was this house!"

"Do you enjoy living in this house?" I asked her.

"Oh yes," she nodded. "I love this house."

I finished up the bathroom and I swept and mopped the kitchen floor. Kathy paid me, and we wished each other a Merry Christmas.

I then took the money and found a fellow on Craigslist selling two kids' bikes - a boy's bike the right size for Sam and a girl's bike the right size for Savannah. I drove out and bought those two bikes and I took them home and stored them for Christmas.

And I grinned a lot, because Kathy had enjoyed what some people would call a Pentecostal experience with a visiting Catholic priest. I thought that was marvelous. I grinned because Kathy had her subjective experience with the love of God too.

CHAPTER 33
MORE ADVENTURES TO COME

It's been four years since we lost Randy, and my son Samuel is now 11-years-old. I picked the children up from the bus last week like usual, and Sam said something interesting. "You know," he told me as we drove home, "bad things are always followed by good things. I lost my Transformer, but then somebody gave me a bigger one. Dad died, but then we got to move here."

"You're glad we moved here?" I asked him.

"Yeah," he said.

Here in November of 2013, we live in a four-bedroom home that I bought for $80,000 on a quiet street in a town where the kids can ride their bikes to the grocery store and pizza place and library. It's a pleasant old home, with built-in china cabinets and leaded windows and oak floors. We know the neighborhood families, and a variety of kids regularly knock on my door asking to play. My children are in a small public school here in the mountains where the teachers can give the students individual attention. All three of my kids are getting straight A's and testing far above their grade levels in reading and math.

I look at little Zekie, and I think, "This child needs a daddy. It's sad and wrong that this little boy is growing up and he doesn't have his daddy." That's a hole that can never be fixed for the children. Their father can't take them fishing, which he loved. He can't teach them carpentry or how to change spark plugs. He can't interrogate the gooey-eyed love interests they bring home. Somebody else, not their dad, will have to do those things. There are several good men in the kids' lives, but their dad doesn't get to be there for them anymore.

Still, all three children love living here, and they seem genuinely happy in their lives.

I might live to be an ancient woman, but my time on earth is limited too. I have to use both hands to count the number of times I've just missed death. I expect to survive the next many close calls, but one day I'll be gone. It's going to happen. I may have another 70 years, but I don't know. I pray God protects me so I don't have to leave my babies, but even then I have to trust He'll take care of them. They've been His little ones all along.

I have an excellent job where I'm learning about geochemistry. I get to drop the kids off at the bus in the morning and go to work, then get off of work and pick them up from the bus in the afternoon. I'm 90 minutes away from the university where Crazy Ernie still teaches a class on invertebrate paleontology. I met him two months ago, and I'm going to learn from one of the world's few experts on Permian bryozoans.

Dr. Stillwell and I are good friends. Sometimes I'll want to call him, and I'll feel in my spirit that it's a bad time. So, I don't. Then, a day or week later, when I'm not expecting it, I'll feel in my spirit that he wants to hear from me. So, I call him, and he invariably says, "Hi Amy Joy! You called me at just the right time!" We will then have a merry conversation about nothing important, and it's just fun. I stop by and see him whenever I'm in West Virginia. I stop in and see Flash and Amanda Gurden too when I'm in town, and I always bring them goat cheese from the Caerphilly farm. My teachers have not been stuck in a corner yet. I still see them.

I don't know how Matthew's vision will play out - the one where God splits a mountain and sends me down a path I don't want to walk. Not a single remarkable thing has happened yet on Thursday. Not yet. I'm going to keep serving God as well as I know how. He's good to me, and I know He will not waste a single tear. He takes dead seeds, and He turns them into beautiful, fragrant flowers. And I'm willing for Him to do whatever He wants in my life as I watch and wait for Him. Because, I believe whatever He wants is beyond anything I could ever hope. I'm confident His plans are absolutely brilliant.

And for some reason, He loves Dr. Stillwell and Dr. Derlidger. He loves Dr. Dan and the Vallos. He loves Dr. Manchester and Flash and their wives and children. In all His wisdom, He might even love Dr. Zenith. I'm sure that if I disappeared off the earth tomorrow, they would all be just fine. And I'm thankful. I'm thankful that they matter to the King of Eternity.

My story about these professors is not over. Remarkable events continued into 2011 and 2012, and I expect another stack of history still lies ahead of us. I hope you look forward to the conclusion of this tale as much as I do. Something big is coming, I'm sure of it.

After all, life goes on during the writing of books.

Term: Fall 2010-2011

Major: Chemistry
Academic Standing: Good Standing

Subject	Course	Level	Title	Grade
BIOL	305	01	Cell Biology	B
CHEM	315	01	Organic Chemistry I	A
CHEM	315L	01	Organic Chem I Lab	A
CHEM	325	01	Computers in Science	A
GSCI	301	01	Physical Geology	A
PHYS	221	01	General Physics	A
PHYS	221L	01	General Physics Lab	A

APPENDIX

I do not pretend to know everything in the world. Every time I open a new can of information, I discover that it is filled to the lid with springy worms that are difficult to stuff back in. All subjects are complex, but I do think the items in this appendix are worth looking at. I hope you enjoy getting some additional ideas on some very deep subjects.

DRUNK GREEKS

First century Jewish historian Josephus begins his work *Against Apion* with a criticism of Greek historians, and he scoffs at those who take Greek "history" seriously. Josephus argues that any fool could go out and write a Greek history, but in his own culture the honor was reserved for the Jewish prophets, who were both inspired by God and dedicated to recording, "a clear account of the events of their own time just as they occurred..."[1]

> We have given practical proof of our reverence for our own Scriptures. For, although such long ages have now passed, no one has ventured either to add, or to remove, or to alter a syllable; and it is an instinct with every Jew, from the day of his birth, to regard them as the decrees of God, to abide by them, and, if need be, cheerfully to die for them.[2]

Would the Greeks die for their histories? Hardly. Josephus roundly boxes the ears of the Greeks, putting their descriptions about recent events - events he himself had experienced - on the same level as boozed-up story telling:

> We have actually had so-called histories even of our recent war published by persons who never visited the sites nor were anywhere near the actions described, but, having put together a few hearsay reports, have, with the gross impudence of drunken revellers, miscalled their productions by the name of history.[3]

Oh, hoh snap! Drunk Greeks!

Josephus expresses great respect for the Scriptures of his people, and with good reason. The books of the Hebrew Bible are not recent creations as Dr. Stillwell suggested. They reach back into ancient times, long long before the birth of Jesus Christ, and there's a lot of evidence for it.

---

1   Josephus, F., Thackery, H.S. Trans. (1926). *Against Apion*, 1:38.
2   *Ibid.*(1:42).
3   *Ibid.*(1:46).

Consider the Septuagint. Ptolemy II (283-246 B.C.) of Alexandria, Egypt had a group of Jewish scholars translate the five books of Moses into Greek. The Hebrew Scriptures were translated before Jesus Christ was born, and the Septuagint (LXX) was widely quoted in the Greek-speaking world of the New Testament. These were not new books being translated for the mere fun of it. They were the venerated Law and Prophets and Writings converted into Greek for the benefit of a world that didn't speak Hebrew. The Aramaic Targums (Aramaic paraphrases and explanations of the Hebrew) were also in translation by the first century.

There were also several Hebrew versions of the Scriptures by the first century. The Jews in Jerusalem scrupulously copied what became the Masoretic Text (MT), the authoritative text of the Hebrew Scriptures today. The Samaritans had their own text of the Torah, the Samaritan Pentateuch (SP), which contained some expanded passages.[4]

Then there are the Dead Sea Scrolls.

The Dead Sea Scrolls were found in caves along the Dead Sea in what is now the West Bank. Sealed clay jars contained some 1200 manuscripts, more than 300 of which contain biblical texts. There are multiple copies of each of the five books of Moses, including versions written in ancient paleo-Hebrew script - that is, the form of Hebrew letters used before the exile to Babylon (605-539 B.C.). In other words, the Dead Sea Scrolls are old, but they themselves are just copies of very ancient texts. The scrolls include fragments of every book in the Old Testament with the exception of Esther. Paleographic studies, which analyze the letters of the words themselves, have placed the ages of most of the scrolls between about 250 B.C. and A.D. 50.[5] Radiocarbon dating efforts have matched the paleographic

---

4   The Septuagint translators in Alexandria apparently used the SP in their work, because the LXX often follows the SP. Clearly, Josephus didn't consider the Samaritans' version worth mentioning when making his defense against Apion. Remember, the Jerusalem Jews and the Samaritans didn't get along well.

5   Especially see Cross, F. (1998). The Palaeography of the Dead Sea Scrolls. In P. Flint & J. VanderKam (Eds.), *The Dead Sea Scrolls after Fifty Years: A Comprehensive Assessment* (Vol. 1, pp. 379-402). Leiden: Brill. Also see Avigad, N. (1958). The Palaeography of the Dead Sea Scrolls and Related Documents. In C. Rabin & Y. Yadin (Eds.), *Aspects of the Dead Sea scrolls,* (pp. 56-87). Jerusalem: Magnes Press, Hebrew University.

dates fairly well[6], and it seems unlikely the community living there in Qumran would have stuck around during the war between the Romans and Jews in A.D. 66-73.

And before that:

In 626 B.C., a former Assyrian official named Nabopolassar set up his capital at Babylon, founding the Babylonian Empire. His son Nebuchadnezzar continued to expand the empire, and he famously conquered the land of Judah and exiled its inhabitants. The Bible describes this period of time extensively.[7]

The Jews' exile to Babylon is a wildly significant, freely acknowledged part of Jewish history. Nebuchadnezzar forcibly moved the Jews to Babylon in waves between 605 and 586 B.C. Remember Daniel in the lion's den? His book begins by describing how he was taken as a boy to serve in the court of King Nebuchadnezzar?[8] His episode with the lions took place many decades later, after the Babylonian Empire had fallen and Daniel was quite an old man. Cyrus the Great took over Babylon in 539 B.C., and the books of Ezra and Nehemiah describe the rebuilding of Jerusalem and the Temple in the years following.

This is important: there are major differences in the written language used before and after the Babylonian captivity, because the writers picked up a lot of Aramaic vocabulary and idioms in Babylon. For instance, the month names changed. The first month of the Hebrew religious calendar has been "Nisan" since Babylon,[9] but before their captivity the Hebrews called it "Abib."[10] When 1 Kings was written, the eighth month was called "Bul" instead of the modern "Heshvan" and the second month was "Ziv" instead of "Iyyar."[11] We do not find the newer month names in books written prior to the Babylonian captivity.

---

6   See Bonani, G. et al. (1992). Radiocarbon Dating of Fourteen Dead Sea Scrolls. *Radiocarbon, 34*(3): 843-849. And T. Jull et al. (1995). Radiocarbon Dating of Scrolls and Linen Fragments from the Judean Desert. *Radiocarbon* 37(1): 11-19.
7   See the end of 2 Kings and 2 Chronicles as well as Jeremiah and Daniel, Ezra, Nehemiah and Esther.
8   Daniel chapter 1.
9   Nehemiah 2:1 and Esther 3:7
10 Exodus 23:15, Deuteronomy 16:1.
11 1 Kings 6

And before that:

Archeological evidence corroborates the biblical history found earlier in Kings and Chronicles. Even Dr. Stillwell himself recognized that the Bible is useful for archeology. Three different books of the Bible describe how the Assyrian king Sennacherib had Jerusalem surrounded by armies in the 8th century B.C., but God saved King Hezekiah and the people of Jerusalem by sending an angel to kill the Assyrians in the middle of the night.[12]

The Taylor Prism (689 B.C.) in the British Museum gives the Assyrian king Sennacherib's description of this siege against Jerusalem, in which he says, "As to Hezekiah, the Jew, he did not submit to my yoke...Himself I made a prisoner in Jerusalem, his royal residence, like a bird in a cage."

Actually, it's kind of entertaining which details the Taylor Prism leaves out. It boasts about how thoroughly the Assyrians had beaten up the Jews and the surrounding peoples, but it doesn't say why the Assyrians suddenly stopped their campaign. Sennacherib increased Hezekiah's tribute and roughed him up, but it's a matter of history that Sennacherib's brutal winning streak halted after Jerusalem - which he never entered and he never took over.

In his *Histories* (440 B.C.), the Greek writer Herodotus stated that when Sennacherib went to fight the Egyptians, mice came up in the middle of the night and ate all the quivers, bowstrings and leather shield straps of the Assyrians so that they retreated the next day when they woke up and found their weapons destroyed.[13]

Of course, Sennacherib didn't say, "I got stomped." That doesn't make for good self-glorification on permanent clay prisms. Sennacherib had already razed Babylon to the ground, but he got stymied at Jerusalem! He didn't progress after that, and that's the bottom line. The end of 2 Kings 19 tells us Esarhaddon took the throne after Sennacherib's own sons killed him. The British Museum has a clay tablet on that too.

---

12   2 Kings 18-19, 2 Chronicles 32 and Isaiah 36-37
13   Herodotus (440 B.C.) *Histories*, 2.141

In my first college go-around, my buddy Roger Altizer and I each wrote papers on a particular battle between Egyptian Pharaoh Ramses II and the Hittites. I researched the Hittites' side and Roger wrote for the Egyptians. Both sides claimed to have won the battle. *Both* sides claimed victory. It was clear, though, that Ramses II had gotten clobbered at one point. The Egyptians did rally for a comeback, but the affair ultimately ended in a stalemate. Ramses II turned around and went home, and the Hittites maintained their liberty. Ramses II didn't conquer the Hittites, but he couldn't admit his own defeat so he put some pro-Egyptian spin on the whole thing.

One of the things I really like about the Bible is its willingness to say, "We got stomped." The Israelites admitted defeat and humiliation, and that's rare in any age. The Bible honestly admits the foolishness and failures of its human heroes. In 2 Kings 18-19, we recognize that Hezekiah was in huge trouble. He'd had to give Sennacherib massive amounts of gold and silver - even stripping the gold from the doors of the holy Temple. It was humiliating, but the Jewish historians admitted this humiliation. Sennacherib failed at Jerusalem, but the Bible doesn't say Hezekiah beat Sennacherib because of his great strength and strategy. The Hebrew accounts declare that Jerusalem was saved by God. That's it.

How can we know when certain Bible books were written? The Bible's authors meticulously dated their works. They offer us a large number of relative dates that give us clues about timelines. 1 Kings 6:1 says:

> *And it came to pass in the four hundred and eightieth year after the children of Israel had come out of the land of Egypt, in the fourth year of Solomon's reign over Israel, in the month of Ziv, which is the second month, that he began to build the house of the LORD.*

That's pretty specific. What's more, 480 years is a short time, historically. Queen Elizabeth I was born in 1533, 480 years from 2013. We haven't lost the history of the Tudors or the works of

Shakespeare in five short centuries. That's the same small space of years from Moses to Solomon. From Solomon's death to the reign of Hezekiah is even shorter - fewer than 230 years.[14]

The difficulty is that the further we go back in time, the harder it is to find archeological correlation to biblical events. It's discouraging when generic titles like "Pharaoh" are used or when ancient king names and dates don't seem to match up. What's more, much of the Holy Land's history has been outright destroyed.

Jerusalem has been burned twice and even plowed over since the time of Solomon. The Second Temple was burned by the Romans in A.D. 70 and completely demolished. Josephus tells us that Jerusalem had been so razed under Rome's Emperor Titus that people could hardly believe anybody had ever lived there.[15]

Still, archeological evidence that Solomon and David actually existed pops up in various places and forms. In 1992, the Tel-Dan Stele was found in northern Israel with a statement by a Syrian king that included reference to the "House of David," indicating David had a dynasty. The Mesha Stele in the Louvre Museum parallels 2 Kings 3:4-8 from the Moabite point of view. It references Yahweh and Israel, including the "House of Omri" and the "House of David." The Amarna tablets excavated in Egypt demonstrate that a Canaanite administration with the diplomatic sophistication of court scribes existed in Jerusalem during the 1300s B.C., during the time when the Hebrews would have been invading the area. These cuneiform letters from Jerusalem tell us the city existed at that time, despite a loss of archeological evidence.[16]

There is an ancient Jewish fortress called Khirbet Qeiyafa above the Valley of Elah, where the Bible says David killed Goliath. Hebrew University and the Israel Antiquities Authority finished excavating the site in 2013 and are now analyzing the finds. Professor Yosef Garfinkel of Hebrew University argues the entire site supports the

---

14 Thiele, E. (1983). *The Mysterious Numbers of the Hebrew Kings*. Grand Rapids: Zondervan/Kregel & Kitchen, K. (2003) *On the Reliability of the Old Testament*. Grand Rapids and Cambridge: William B. Eerdmans Publishing Company.
15 Josephus, *Jewish War*, 7:1:1
16 Naaman, N. (1996). The Contribution of the Amarna Letters to the Debate on Jerusalem's Political Position in the Tenth Century B. C. E. *Bulletin of the American Schools of Oriental Research*, (304): 17-27.

existence of a historic King David whose reign matches what the Bible describes.[17]

So, why doubt the historicity of the Bible? After all, the children of Israel have protected their Scriptures and dutifully copied them for millennia.

One huge issue is that the prophets of the Bible make prophecies that actually come true after the dates on their books.

DANIEL

It's easy to say that Daniel was written after the fact. It's quite easy to say, and many people say it. Daniel is placed in the historical section of the Hebrew Scriptures, not the prophetic section. Daniel details events that took place after the death of Alexander the Great, even though Daniel didn't even live to see Alexander.[18] His book accurately portrays history in advance, but he also writes that angels came to him and gave him descriptions of future kingdoms. Modern scholars reject the supernatural claims of Daniel, and most date the book of Daniel to the time of the Maccabees in the 2nd century B.C. (400 years after the author of Daniel claims to have lived).

However, there are serious problems with putting Daniel in the 2nd century B.C., because internal and external evidences point to a much earlier date.

For instance, the Hebrew and Aramaic of Daniel are far older than that which was used during the Greek Empire. It's like the difference between King James English and English today. Kenneth Kitchen places Daniel's Aramaic between the 7th and 4th centuries B.C. in Babylon,[19] before Alexander the Great conquered the known world. Daniel uses certain Persian words as well, and these were so old by the time of the Septuagint that the translators mistranslated them. Reverend Edward Pusey made a good point about this in 1886:

---

17 Garfinkel, Y., & Ganor, S. (2008). Khirbet Qeiyafa: Sha`arayim. *Journal of Hebrew Scriptures*, 8(22): 1-10.// Garfinkel, Y., Streit, K., Ganor, S., & Hasel, M. (2012). State Formation in Judah: Biblical Tradition, Modern Historical Theories, and Radiometric Dates at Khirbet Qeiyafa. *Radiocarbon*, 54(3–4): 359-369// Garfinkel, Y. (2011). The Birth & Death of Biblical Minimalism. *Biblical Archaeology Review*, 37(3): 46–53, 78.

18 Daniel 8:20ff; Daniel 11

19 Kitchen, K. (1965). The Aramaic of Daniel. In D. J. Wiseman (Ed.), *Notes on Some Problems in the Book of Daniel* (p. 79). London: The Tyndale Press.

Those who invent a later date for the Book of Daniel can attempt no real explanation how a Jew who, according to their hypothesis, lived in Palestine about 163 B.C., should be acquainted with Aryan [Iranian] words, which related to offices which had long ceased to exist, or to dress which no one wore, words which were mostly obliterated from Aramaic, which (as far as they survived) were inherited only from Daniel's text; and several of them were misunderstood or not understood by Aramaic translators....[20]

Even more obvious, Daniel's Greek loan words are noticeably scant and are limited to musical instruments. Remember, the Greek Empire dominated the Middle East since the time of Alexander in the 4th century before Christ. Greek was the trade language. Imagine if Italy had ruled over America for the past 200 years. Our Italian vocabulary would extend far beyond *piano* and *pizza* and *ravioli*. We don't all speak Italian, because it's not the trade language of the known world. We can tell that Greek was not the trade language of Daniel's world, because he's glaringly shy on his Greek. Besides those musical instruments, there are no other Greek loan words.

Scholars commonly state that Daniel was written right after the Maccabean revolt in 167 B.C., and yet several copies of Daniel were found in the Dead Sea Scrolls, just like Genesis and other highly venerated books.[21]

Harvard professor Frank Cross was particularly struck by one of the Daniel manuscripts. Cross accepts the basic 2nd century date for Daniel, and therefore assumes he has a copy of a very recently written book. He notes:

One copy of Daniel is inscribed in the script of the late second century BC; in some ways its antiquity is more striking than that of the oldest manuscripts from Qumran, since it is no more than about half a century younger than the autograph of Daniel.[22]

20   Pusey, E. (1868). *Daniel the Prophet: Nine Lectures Delivered in the Divinity School of the University of Oxford, 2nd Ed.* (xlii, 38). Oxford: James Parker & Co.
21   Hasel, G. (1992, January) New Light on the Book of Daniel from the Dead Sea Scrolls. *Bible and Spade.*
22   Cross, F. (1995) *The Ancient Library of Qumran, 3rd Ed.* Sheffield, England: Sheffield Academic Press, 43.

That's precisely the issue. It's unlikely the Essenes would have venerated the book of Daniel only 50 years from the date it was written. Even Esther, dated to the 4th century B.C., didn't make it into the Dead Sea Scrolls. In contrast, the Essene community honored Daniel enough to include at least eight manuscripts in its collection, and these contained none of the Septuagint's Greek apocryphal additions. This strongly suggests that Daniel is much older than the 2nd century.

It's incorrect to give Daniel's book a late date just because he offers accurate descriptions of Greek events long before the Greek Empire dominated the world. He claimed divine revelation, and his accounts proved true. A bias against divine revelation is just that. It's a bias.

It's clearly wrong to approach the Bible with the attitude, "Predictive prophecy is impossible. This must have been written after the fact." That's ridiculous. It's important to look at the actual evidence of the book and determine its date. Each book was written whenever it was written. A researcher's belief or disbelief in predictive prophecy has nothing to do with anything.

DID ISAIAH HAVE A TWIN?

The book of Isaiah is one of the greatest literary works in ancient history and, like Daniel, it speaks of events that took place centuries after its named author had died. Many scholars assume that the foretelling portions of Isaiah were written later. Critics have divided the book of Isaiah into (at least) two parts, Proto-Isaiah and Deutero-Isaiah.

The common view on the authorship of Isaiah is that Isaiah son of Amoz dealt with the issues of his day, while another person writing under Isaiah's name spoke to events that took place a couple centuries later. There is a bit of a "bridge" of narrative in chapters 36-39, and Isaiah does not name himself after chapter 39, so Proto-Isaiah is generally credited with chapters 1-39. Deutero-Isaiah is believed to have written chapters 40-66, which come after the bridge. Some even argue for a Trito-Isaiah that takes chapters 56-66.

Proto-Isaiah is considered a doom and gloom Isaiah before the Babylonian captivity, one who is all about the punishment of the idolatrous Jews, and Deutero-Isaiah is viewed as a comforting prophet after the Babylonian captivity, one who sees the mercy of God in a later time.

According to George Livingston Robinson, some groups of scholars have agreed that Isaiah son of Amoz wrote about 22 chapters of the 66 credited to his name.[23] Other critics have argued he hardly wrote a bit of it. Robinson states:

> The radical wing of the critical school, which is represented by Drs. Cheyne, Duhm, Hackmann, Guthe, and Marti, rejects approximately 1030 verses out of the total 1292 in the book, retaining the following only as *the genuine produce of Isaiah and his age*: 1:2-26, 29-31; 2:6-19; 3:1,5,8,9,12-17, 24; 4:1; 5:1-14,17-29; 6:1-13; 7:1-8:22; 9:8-10:9; 10:13,14,27-32; 14:24-32; 17:1-14; 18:1-6; 20:1-6; 22:1-22; 28:1-4,7-22; 29:1-6,9,10,13-15; 30:1-17; 31:1-4. That is, only about 262 verses out of the total 1292 are allowed to be genuine.[24]

23 Robinson, G. (1954). Study Five: The Critical Problem. In *The book of Isaiah: In fifteen studies* (Rev. ed., p. 59). Grand Rapids: Baker Book House. Italics were in the original.

24 *Ibid*, p 59-60.

Really? They're confident Isaiah wrote verses 3:1 and 3:5 and 3:8, but not the verses in between? I'm always puzzled by the textual critics. It seems strange that any honest scholar would feel free to throw out 80% of a book that had been respected for the 2700 years before he came along. That's just crazy.

FOREVER AND EVER

According to Robinson, these critics assume any prophet should have written only about the matters that pertained to his own day and age. They argue that the real Isaiah wouldn't have tried to convert the heathen or speak of God's judging the whole earth. He wouldn't have portrayed the "picture of universal peace."

Hastings Bible Dictionary quotes biblical critic A.B. Davidson's summary on the matter:

> The prophet is always a man of his own time and it is always to the people of his own time that he speaks, not to a generation long after, not to us. And the things of which he speaks will always be things of importance to the people of his own day, whether they be things belonging to their internal life and conduct, or things affecting their external fortunes as a people among other peoples.[25]

It seems the book of Isaiah has a habit of ignoring 19th-20th century rules about what prophets were supposed to do. It's not that Isaiah didn't speak to some of the biggest issues of his day - idolatry, injustice, oppression - because he did. But these critics simply ignore the book's own claim to be speaking to future generations:

> *Now go, write it before them in a table, and note it in a book, that it may be for the time to come for ever and ever:*
>
> Isaiah 30:8

> *The grass withereth, the flower fadeth: but the word of our God shall stand for ever.*
>
> Isaiah 40:8

---

25 As quoted in Allis, O. (1951). *The Unity of Isaiah. (A study in prophecy.)* (p. 2). Eugene, OR: Wipf and Stock.

The Hebrew *ad 'olam* can be translated "as far as eternity" or "into perpetuity." In verse 30:8 Isaiah says, *ad ad 'olam*, with the second "ad" for emphasis, which is why it's been translated "forever and ever."

It's true that the job of a prophet is *not* primarily to tell the future. His job is to speak to the people on God's behalf. He's God's mouthpiece. However, that doesn't preclude warnings about the future - or speaking to future generations. If the prophet is really God's mouthpiece, then God can speak to whomever He wants throughout time and space.

Beyond this, the problem with hacking up Isaiah is that there are few literary or historical reasons to do it. The language is all pre-Babylonian, without Aramaic loan words. The geography is that of mountainous Israel and not flat Fertile Crescent. Isaiah uses similar vocabulary throughout the whole book. There's plenty of internal evidence to support the single authorship of Isaiah.

The irony is that the very chapters credited to Deutero-Isaiah are the chapters in which God repeatedly points to His power to predict the future as evidence of His reality as the one and only true God. He's serious about this issue, and His words make little sense if they were written after the events took place.

> *I have declared the former things from the beginning; They*
> *went forth from My mouth, and I caused them to hear it.*
> *Suddenly I did them, and they came to pass. Because I knew*
> *that you were obstinate, And your neck was an iron sinew,*
> *And your brow bronze, Even from the beginning I have*
> *declared it to you; Before it came to pass I proclaimed it to you*
> *....*
>
> -Isaiah 48:3-5

Consider Isaiah 45, in which Isaiah gives a message from Yahweh to Cyrus the Persian. (I am so impressed with this passage):

> *... Who says of Cyrus, 'He is My shepherd, And he shall*
> *perform all My pleasure, Saying to Jerusalem, "You shall be*
> *built," And to the temple, "Your foundation shall be laid." '*
>
> -Isaiah 44:28

Thus saith the LORD to his anointed, to Cyrus, whose right hand I have holden, to subdue nations before him; and I will loose the loins of kings, to open before him the two leaved gates; and the gates shall not be shut...For Jacob my servant's sake, and Israel mine elect, I have even called thee by thy name: I have surnamed thee, though thou hast not known me. I am the LORD, and there is none else, there is no God beside me: I girded thee, though thou hast not known me: That they may know from the rising of the sun, and from the west, that there is none beside me. I am the LORD, and there is none else.

-Isaiah 45:1,4-6[26]

It is a matter of secular history that Cyrus the Great took over Babylon without a battle in 539 B.C., walking right into the city. In the Cyrus Cylinder (also in the British Museum), Cyrus describes how he entered Babylon and then let all manner of unnamed people go back home to their lands - that he allowed them to rebuild their sanctuaries. The Cyrus Cylinder doesn't mention the Jews or Jerusalem by name, but it offers warm wishes of peace toward all the people of all those lands and their gods and their dwelling places.

Isaiah the son of Amoz was dead by about 700 B.C., 100 years before Cyrus the Great was born. Jerusalem and the Temple were still *standing* in Isaiah's day. Solomon's Temple would not be destroyed until the Babylonians demolished it in 586 B.C., generations after Isaiah's death, yet Isaiah prophesied long in advance that a king named Cyrus would have the Temple rebuilt. Many academics have read the Cyrus passages in Isaiah and argued that they must have been added to the book long after the dusting of its original author.

Except.

Except, this passage calls on Cyrus "by name" to prove that Yahweh is God, even though Cyrus didn't know Yahweh and didn't claim Him. The passage makes the case that the very act of calling

---

26 This is the King James Version. The NKJV states, "loose the armor of kings," and I don't think that's the best translation. "Loose the loins of kings" is more literal - a bit more graphic and descriptive of the sort of fear Cyrus would inflict.

Cyrus by his name is sufficient to let the world know that Yahweh is God. That doesn't make sense if the whole world already knew that Cyrus was a friendly chap who encouraged his subjects to rebuild their homelands.

The very wording used in his cylinder suggests Cyrus knew of the passage in Isaiah. Cyrus says, "He took the hand of Cyrus, king of the city of Anshan, and called him by his name, proclaiming him aloud for the kingship over all of everything." Cyrus thanks his god Marduk "king of the whole of heaven and earth" extensively and not Yahweh. But, Yahweh notes, "I girded thee, though thou hast not known me," so that the rest of the world would get it, even if Cyrus did not.

A God Outside Time

This is serious. Isaiah claims to be a prophet hearing from a God who knows the end from the beginning.[27] We can't flick away that claim and assume that there's a second or third author just because Isaiah describes the future centuries in advance; that's precisely how Isaiah's God says we can know He's the real God - as opposed to the idols the people had been worshiping.[28]

The textual critics generally reject the possibility that Isaiah was actually hearing from the eternal God. With every frank cell in my body, I insist that biblical criticism should have no bias either way. The analysts are in no position to determine whether Isaiah spoke directly with God. Period. Judgments about the book's authorship should be based on clear internal and external evidence and not on the fancies and personal opinions of people with swollen heads.

The Isaiah Scroll

Isaiah should only be chopped up if there are historical and literary reasons to do so. What evidence do we see?

In the Dead Sea Scrolls, the entire book of Isaiah was found rolled up together in one large scroll, without even a space between

---

27 Isaiah 46:10
28 Isaiah 41:22-29;42:8-9; 45:1-6

chapters 39 and 40. In his book *The Unity of Isaiah*, Oswald Allis makes a little dig, "Obviously the scribe was not conscious of the alleged fact that an important change of situation, involving an entire change of authorship, begins with chapter 40."[29]

Throughout all of history, there was never any question about the authorship of Isaiah. Even old A. B. Davidson recognized this fact, stating, "For nearly twenty-five centuries no one dreamt of doubting that Isaiah, the son of Amoz, was the author of every part of the book that goes under his name."[30] The Great Isaiah Scroll is, in fact, divided into two parts, one ending at our modern version's chapter 33 and the next beginning at chapter 34. That's hardly significant, though. The end of chapter 33 is halfway through the 66 chapter book.

The real question is, "does a different author obviously take over at some point?"

Isaiah does change tone as he switches back and forth from rebuke to comfort, rebuke and comfort. He also wrote during the reigns of several kings, over the course of many years (Isaiah 1:1), which also might affect his tone as he got softer in his old age. However, the book itself points to a single author.

LANGUAGE AND VOCABULARY

For instance, Isaiah calls God, "The Holy One of Israel" equally in both halves of the 66 chapters. It's Isaiah's favorite name for God, used 12 times in chapters 1-39 and 14 times in chapters 40-66. The phrase is only used six other times in the Bible outside of Isaiah.

Isaiah son of Amoz lived in Judah during the 8th century B.C. If a Deutero-Isaiah wrote the second part of the book, then he lived during the Babylonian exile in the 6th century and after. It should be easy to demonstrate a late date for Deutero-Isaiah by showing the Babylonian influence of his writings, but we don't see that influence. While Isaiah focuses a great deal on the captivity in Babylon and God's deliverance, he doesn't use Babylonian vocabulary the way that

---

29 Allis, O. (1951). *The Unity of Isaiah. (A study in prophecy.)* (p. 40). Eugene, OR: Wipf and Stock. Allis does much better job of covering all these matters than I do in my little appendix jottings.

30 In Robinson, G.L. 1954. *The Book of Isaiah*. Grand Rapids, MI: Baker, p 59.

post-exilic prophets do. We don't see Babylonian words or idioms in Isaiah. The vocabulary used throughout the book is pure Hebrew.

SUBJECT MATTER

It seems strange that Isaiah talks so much about Babylon, since Assyria was the big enemy during Isaiah's lifetime. Babylon wouldn't be a problem for another century. Yet, the focus on Babylon starts early in the book, clear back in chapter 13, when Isaiah says, *"The burden of Babylon, which Isaiah the son of Amoz did see."* Babylon comes up in both the beginning and the end of the 66 chapters.

We find a similar "non-pattern" regarding many of Isaiah's themes. He goes back and forth, bringing up the same issues over and over throughout the book. While the first 39 chapters of Isaiah are generalized as doom and gloom, they contain plenty of hope, and while the final chapters are considered the chapters of hope, they also contain plenty of rebuke. The prophecies go back and forth from, "I have to punish you," to "but I'm going to forgive and heal you," over and over.

We also find that idolatry is a big subject all throughout Isaiah[31] but it's *not* a subject in the post-exilic books of Ezra, Haggai or Zechariah where idolatry was an issue of the past.

Radical critics aside, it's generally recognized that Isaiah son of Amoz wrote the first 39 chapters, but in verse 3:8, Isaiah speaks of Jerusalem as already fallen and destroyed in the prophetic future. Again in 6:11-13, God describes the return of the remnant of Judah after the destruction of the land. On the other hand, passages like 40:9 and 62:6 treat Jerusalem and the cities of Judah as standing and strong.

LITERARY SKILL

What's more, Isaiah is considered one of the greatest writers of the ancient world. He used an extensive, colorful vocabulary, and he must have had some rank to have had access to the king. His book is a masterpiece of visual description and metaphor, parable

---

31   Isaiah 41:29; 44:9-20; 57:4ff; 65:2-7

and poetry, diatribe and dialogue, and his skills do not diminish as he progresses from chapter to chapter through to the end.

Isaiah is filled, from chapter 1 to chapter 66, with passages that use a chiastic structure. Think of chiastic structure as a literary parallelogram. Parallelograms are words or sentences that are the same forward and backwards, like "mom", "bob", or "step on no pets." Chiastic structure in Hebrew poetry is also the same forwards and backwards. Consider Isaiah 6:10 or chapter 44:[32]

Isaiah 6:10
A. Make the *heart* of this people fat,
   B. and make their *ears* heavy,
      C. and shut their *eyes*;
      C'. lest they see with their *eyes*,
   B'. and hear with their *ears*,
A'. and understand with their *heart*, and return, and be healed.

Isaiah 44
A. (44:2) "Thus saith the LORD that made thee, and formed thee from the womb…"
   B. (44:2) "Fear not, O Jacob, my servant;"
      C (44:10) "a graven image that is profitable for nothing"
         D. (44:12-17) (Fools make a god and worships it.)
      C' (44:20) "Is there not a lie in my right hand?"
   B' (44:21) "O Jacob and Israel; for thou art my servant"
A' (44:24) "the LORD, thy redeemer, and he that formed thee from the womb."

Isaiah uses chiastic structure extensively throughout the 66 chapters of his book. It's all over the place, and the purpose of this form of Hebrew poetry is to emphasize a point. Chiasms are often like an hourglass with the big, main focal point in the middle. In Isaiah, chiasms can be found contained in one verse, or they start in one chapter and end in another.

---

32 I've used the old King James Version in the verses to the end of this section.

Isaiah also uses parallel couplets throughout. These are repetitive phrases that offer the same concept twice in a row, each with a different nuance of meaning. It's a poetic form of writing that hammers home an idea, lest there be any confusion about his intended meaning. Consider these two couplets from Isaiah 53:5:

But he was *wounded* for our *transgressions*,
he was *bruised* for our *iniquities*...

...the *chastisement* of our *peace* was upon him;
and with his *stripes* we are *healed*.

Isaiah offers the same idea twice in a row in each couplet. In the first, Isaiah makes it clear that the protagonist of the chapter is taking the punishment for our sins. In the second, he lets us know how much we benefit; our peace comes from his punishment; we're healed because he's beaten. This parallel imagery is one of Isaiah's favorite writing styles.

Isaiah 5:7a-b:
For the vineyard of the LORD of hosts is the house of Israel,
and the men of Judah his pleasant plant:

and he looked for judgment[33], but behold oppression;
for righteousness, but behold a cry.

Isaiah 55:7
Let the wicked forsake his way,
and the unrighteous man his thoughts:

and let him return unto the LORD, and he will have mercy upon him;
and to our God, for he will abundantly pardon.

---

33 "Judgment" in the King James is what we would call "justice." The LORD's prophets constantly demanded justice for the poor and oppressed and denounced human greed and violence.

Other Hebrew writers employ chiastic structure and parallelism. The Psalms are full of both of these and other poetic forms. Hebrew writing is largely poetic. Isaiah uses these poetic styles extensively with great skill throughout the entire book. He's consistent about it, and it's a hallmark of his writing style. (Many poets have written sonnets in iambic pentameter, but Shakespeare really owned this bit of poetic prowess.)

This is an important point, because the writer of the second half of Isaiah is just as brilliant as the writer of the first half. If the end of the book was written by somebody else hundreds of years after the first Isaiah, then one of the greatest literary geniuses of all of history has gone unnamed. Even when Ezra and Nehemiah were bound together, those two books did not get confused and lumped together under one name. But Deutero Isaiah didn't get his own book like Ezekiel or Zechariah or Haggai. Isaiah son of Amoz was always credited with all of his book - the whole thing - until recent scholars decided they knew better.

As Gleason Archer Jr. declared, "There is not a shred of internal evidence to support the theory of a Second Isaiah, apart from a philosophical prejudice against the possibility of predictive prophecy."[34]

---

34 Archer, G. 1962. Isaiah. *The Wycliffe Bible Commentary*. Chicago, IL: Moody.

THE AUTHORSHIP OF THE GOSPELS:

It's easy to wonder if Matthew, Mark, Luke and John actually wrote the books credited to them. It's valuable to know they were accepted by the church very early on, long before Constantine became the emperor of the Roman Empire and legalized Christianity. We have testimony from the early church fathers regarding the authors of the Gospels. Fewer than 150 years after Christ, in about A.D.180, Irenaeus of Lyons wrote:

> Matthew also issued a written Gospel among the Hebrews in their own dialect, while Peter and Paul were preaching in Rome and laying the foundation of the Church. After their departure, Mark, the disciple and interpreter of Peter, did also hand down to us in writing what had been preached by Peter. Luke also, the companion of Paul, recorded in a book the Gospel preached by him. Afterwards John, the disciple of the Lord, who also had leaned upon his breast, did himself publish a Gospel during his residence at Ephesus in Asia. [35]

John didn't even die until A.D. 100, within a generation of Irenaeus. The apostles were the spiritual grandfathers of these early Christians, men still persecuted by Rome and shunned by the world.

The historian Eusebius quotes earlier church fathers extensively in his *Historia Ecclesiae* ("Church History") accepting their testimonies about who wrote which books. He cites Papias, Bishop of Hierapolis in Asia Minor (c. A.D. 60 - 130):

> "This also the presbyter said: Mark, having become the interpreter of Peter, wrote down accurately, though not indeed in order, whatsoever he remembered of the things done or said by Christ. For he neither heard the Lord nor followed him, but afterward, as I said, he followed Peter, who adapted his teaching to the needs of his hearers, but with no intention of giving a connected account of the Lord's discourses, so that Mark committed no error while he thus wrote some things as he remembered them.

35 Irenaeus of Lyons (AD 175-185). *Against Heresies* 3:1:1.

For he was careful of one thing, not to omit any of the things which he had heard, and not to state any of them falsely." These things are related by Papias concerning Mark.

But concerning Matthew he writes as follows: "So then Matthew wrote the oracles in the Hebrew language, and every one interpreted them as he was able."[36]

I think it's great that Papias says to trust the events in Mark, but not their order. Thank you, Papias. Eusebius also quotes Clement of Alexandria (A.D. 150-215), an early Christian theologian at the Catechetical School of Alexandria. Regarding the Gospels, he said:

Clement gives the tradition of the earliest presbyters, as to the order of the Gospels, in the following manner: "The Gospels containing the genealogies [i.e. Matthew and Luke], he says, were written first. The Gospel according to Mark had this occasion. As Peter had preached the Word publicly at Rome, and declared the Gospel by the Spirit, many who were present requested that Mark, who had followed him for a long time and remembered his sayings, should write them out. And having composed the Gospel he gave it to those who had requested it. When Peter learned of this, he neither directly forbade nor encouraged it. But, last of all, John, perceiving that the external facts had been made plain in the Gospel, being urged by his friends, and inspired by the Spirit, composed a spiritual Gospel." This is the account of Clement.[37]

It's notable that each of the four Gospels are written in different styles with their own focuses. They tell many of the same stories, and the first three Gospels appear to have used some common sources, but they are also each unique.

It's clear that, as Papias said, Matthew was written in Hebrew or Aramaic and then translated into Greek; it's filled with Jewish terminology and it's thoroughly Hebrew in nature. It also contains

---

36 Eusebius, *Church History* 3.39.14-17
37 *Ibid.* 6.14.5-7

long discourses not contained in the other gospels. Matthew was originally a tax collector which required him to have record-keeping skills,[38] and it has been suggested that he took down Jesus' teachings verbatim in shorthand.[39]

Mark was not an eye-witness of Jesus, but early church fathers unanimously state he was with Peter and wrote down Peter's account of the ministry of Jesus of Nazareth. His gospel is visual and action-oriented and omits much that is found in Matthew and Luke.

Luke's gospel and the book of Acts are two letters written to a certain "Theophilus" with the stated purpose of giving Theophilus confidence in the truth of what he's been told about Jesus. Pay attention to this opening statement, because while Luke was not an eye-witness to Jesus' ministry, he tells us that in his own time there were eye witnesses who had worked to record the things they'd seen. What's more, he has directly communicated with those eye witnesses, and he has investigated the matter himself:

> *Inasmuch as many have taken in hand to set in order a narrative of those things which have been fulfilled among us, just as those who from the beginning were eyewitnesses and ministers of the word delivered them to us, it seemed good to me also, having had perfect understanding of all things from the very first, to write to you an orderly account, most excellent Theophilus, that you may know the certainty of those things in which you were instructed.*
>
> Luke 1:1-4

When he says, "from the very first," he means it. The first two chapters of his gospel indicate that he spoke with Mary the mother of Jesus. He tells us things that only Mary would have known, and he says that Mary pondered certain things and kept them "*in her heart.*"[40] That's a very private thing to comment on, and it indicates a personal connection.

---

38 Matthew was also known as "Levi." Matthew 10:3; Luke 5:27
39 Thiede, C., & Ancona, M. (1997). *The Jesus Papyrus* (pp. 158-159). Phoenix.
40 Luke 2:19,51.

There are debates about why Luke's genealogy of Jesus in chapter 3 is so different than Matthew's chapter 1 genealogy, but at least we know they didn't just copy each other. It's exceptionally interesting to me that Luke goes back through David's son Nathan, Solomon's full brother.[41] Luke recognized Jesus as the Christ, the heir of David, but he didn't go through Solomon. That's a worthy study in itself, because it's completely unexpected.

Luke missed out on seeing Jesus in person, but he was a companion of Paul, and he enters the narrative himself in Acts 16:10.[42] The early church fathers unanimously credited the book to Luke, and their testimony is supported by the vocabulary that Luke uses. Both his gospel and Acts use excellent Greek and a large vocabulary filled with medical terminology.[43]

And John. John writes his gospel later in life, but he says, "Hey, I saw this myself."[44] He begins his first epistle by saying, "*That which was from the beginning, which we have heard, which we have seen with our eyes, which we have looked upon, and our hands have handled, concerning the Word of life—*" He repeatedly calls himself "the disciple whom Jesus loved," which shows a personal connection to the man from Galilee.[45]

Are there some minor contradictions in the Gospels? Sure, and that's a good thing. When two eye-witnesses to a car accident give their testimonies, they'll have seen things from different angles and they'll focus on different aspects of the event. One will hear one part of a conversation, and the other will hear another part. There have been many books published on the authorship of the Gospels. I recently came across *Cold Case Christianity* by J. Warner Wallace, which deals with the Gospels from the point of view of a cold case detective. *The Case for Christ*, by Lee Strobel and Josh McDowell's *More Than a Carpenter* are also pleasant reads. The reason I point out

---

41 1Chronicles 3:5
42 Cf. Acts 16:10–17; 20:5–15; 21:1–18; 27:1–28; 28:1-16; Philemon 1:24, 2 Timothy 4:11
43 Cf. Hobart, W. (1882, 2004). *The Medical Language of St. Luke.* Eugene, OR: Wipf and Stock Publishers // Harnack, A., & Wilkinson, J. (1908). *Luke the Physician: The Author of the Third Gospel and the Acts of the Apostles.* New York: G.P. Putnam's Sons.
44 John 21:24
45 John 19:26, 20:2, 21:7,20

these particular books is because all three of these guys had rejected God and the Bible at one point in their lives, and their investigations led them to faith. I just think that's fun.

THE NEBULAR THEORY

The Solar Nebular Theory is the current favorite explanation about how our solar system formed from a nebula, a giant cloud of interstellar dust and gas. It's said that gravitational attraction between particles in the nebular cloud caused them to draw together until they collapsed inward to form the sun. Then, about 4.5 billion years ago a tail of material ejected from the young sun, creating a protoplanetary disk. Lumpy areas formed a multitude of planetesimals, and the planets and many of their moons formed from these smaller bodies. The heaviest elements accreted into the small terrestrial planets nearest the sun, where the solar wind blew away the lighter hydrogen and helium into the outer solar system. As the cores of the outer planets formed, they collected these gasses and formed gas giants.

Brent Dalrymple has a well-known book *The Age of the Earth*, in which he age-dates chondrites in the effort to determine how long Earth has been swinging around the sun.[46] Chondrites are a particularly handy form of space rock believed to have been made from the same material as the sun and the solar nebula, and thus the age of chondrites should be very close to the age of Earth.

It turns out there are innumerable variables to take into consideration when analyzing the Solar Nebular Theory (SNT), however, and innumerable models have been formed to answer its obvious problems. I just want to focus on the few that seem the most difficult to resolve.

OXYGEN

For instance, the sun has more oxygen than expected. In 2004, NASA's Genesis mission discovered that oxygen levels from solar wind debris were surprisingly high. The common O-16 oxygen isotope is far denser in the sun than in Earth, Earth's moon, or Mars.[47] NASA researcher Kevin McKeegan explained:

---

46   Dalrymple, B.G. (1991). *The Age of the Earth* (p. 267). Stanford: Stanford University Press.
47   McKeegan, K et al. (2011). The Oxygen Isotopic Composition of the Sun Inferred from Captured Solar Wind. *Science*, 332(6037): 1528-1532.

We found that Earth, the moon, as well as Martian and other meteorites which are samples of asteroids, have a lower concentration of the O-16 than does the sun… The implication is that we did not form out of the same solar nebula materials that created the sun – just how and why remains to be discovered.[48]

Angular Momentum

One of the best recognized problems with the Solar Nebular Theory is that nearly all the angular momentum in the solar system is found in the planets. The sun has basically all the mass, which means it should have all the angular momentum. But it doesn't. The sun's rotational angular momentum is just 1.10×10^{42} kg m^2/s while the total orbital angular momentum of the planets is much larger at 3.15×10^{43} kg m^2/s. (I've included the dwarf planet Pluto in the following table because NASA lists it in its Planetary Fact Sheet from whence I collected this data. It makes little impact because it's so small, but I'm fond of Pluto.)

The combined mass of all the planets is 2.67×10^{27} kg. The sun has a mass of 1.99×10^{30} kg. Do quick math: the sun's mass is more than 745 times the mass of *all* the planets. Yet, more than 96% of the angular momentum in the solar system is in the planets. Think of an ice skater who goes into a spin. As she pulls her arms in, bringing her center of mass inward, she spins faster. That's not what we see in the solar system. It's the planets that are out there zooming around the sun while the sun spins slowly for its great mass. If the planets sprang from the solar nebula, we'd expect the sun to be spinning rapidly and the momentum of the outer planets to be negligible.

---

48 Agle, D.C. (June 23, 2011). NASA Mission Suggests Sun and Planets Constructed Differently. (Jet Propulsion Laboratory) *Mission News*. Last accessed January 14, 2018 at https://www.nasa.gov/centers/jpl/news/genesis20110623.html .

Table 1 - NASA Planetary Facts [49]			
Planet	**Planet mass (kg)**	**Distance from sun (m)**	**Orbital Velocity (m/s)**	**Orbital Angular Momentum (kg m²/s)**
Mercury	3.30×10^{23}	5.79×10^{10}	4.74×10^{4}	9.06×10^{38}
Venus	4.87×10^{24}	1.08×10^{11}	3.50×10^{4}	1.84×10^{40}
Earth	5.97×10^{24}	1.50×10^{11}	2.98×10^{4}	2.66×10^{40}
Mars	6.42×10^{23}	2.28×10^{11}	2.41×10^{4}	3.53×10^{39}
Jupiter	1.90×10^{27}	7.79×10^{11}	1.31×10^{4}	1.94×10^{43}
Saturn	5.68×10^{26}	1.43×10^{12}	9.70×10^{3}	7.90×10^{42}
Uranus	8.68×10^{25}	2.87×10^{12}	6.80×10^{3}	1.70×10^{42}
Neptune	1.02×10^{26}	4.50×10^{12}	5.40×10^{3}	2.49×10^{42}
Pluto	1.46×10^{22}	5.91×10^{12}	4.70×10^{3}	4.05×10^{38}
Total	2.67×10^{27}			3.15×10^{43}

Cosmologists have spent decades trying to resolve the angular momentum problem, and to my knowledge none of the possible explanations really work so far.

PLANET SPIN AND TILT

What's more, the spin-rates of the planets and their axial tilts are all over the board.

---

49 *NASA Planetary Fact Sheet.* Last accessed November 1, 2017 at https://nssdc.gsfc.nasa.gov/planetary/factsheet/. Angular Momentum is calculated as Mass (kg) x Radius of Orbit (m) x Orbital Velocity (m/s).

Table 2 - More Planetary Facts [50]				
Planet	Planet mass (kg)	Rotation (hours)	Axial Tilt	Year (Earth days)
Mercury	3.30×10^{23}	1407.6	0.034°	88.0
Venus	4.87×10^{24}	-5832.5	177.4°	224.7
Earth	5.97×10^{24}	23.9	23.4°	365.2
Mars	6.42×10^{23}	24.6	25.2°	687.0
Jupiter	1.90×10^{27}	9.90	3.10°	4331
Saturn	5.68×10^{26}	10.7	26.7°	10,747
Uranus	8.68×10^{25}	-17.2	97.8°	30,589
Neptune	1.02×10^{26}	16.1	28.3°	59,800
Pluto	1.46×10^{22}	-153.3	122.5°	90,560

Look at the variations. Venus and Earth are almost the same size, but Earth's day is just under 24 hours, while Venus rotates (backwards) just once during 243 Earth days, which is longer than its year. Because it rotates in reverse, Venus is regarded as though it's upside-down. Check out Jupiter! It spins once on its axis every 9.9 hours. That's impressive, considering Jupiter's size. Saturn's not far behind with a rotation of 10.7 hours. Uranus is on its side and Pluto is tilted on its shoulder. These three, Venus, Uranus, and Pluto are all considered to have retrograde rotation, which is why their rotations are given as negative numbers. For the record, the sun's axial tilt is about 6°.

Earth, Mars, Saturn and Neptune all have fairly similar axial tilts between 23.4° and 28.3°. They are similar to each other even though they're not similar to the sun in this respect. Earth and Mars also rotate at a similar rate, although Mars has just more than 1/10 the mass of Earth. Uranus and Neptune are close to the same size, and Uranus spins at about the same rate as Neptune, but on its side at about 98°.

The retrograde motions of Venus and Uranus have long puzzled astronomers. Venus' rotation is believed to have slowed and reversed due to tides caused by the sun's pull on the planet's heavy atmosphere.[51]

---

50 These data are from the same *NASA Planetary Fact Sheet*. For Rotation and Axial Tilt, I reported to either one decimal place or three significant figures.

51 Ingersoll, A. and Dobrovolskis, A.R. (1978) Venus' Rotation and Atmospheric Tides. *Nature*, 275: 37-38.

Yet, the rotation of Venus seems to have been slowing down in recent years, reversing the reverse so to speak, and that's a real puzzle too.[52]

Uranus is tilted at 98°, but so are its moons! This is a big deal, because even if Uranus got whacked by another planet at one point in its history, that wouldn't have affected the moons. The impact might have tilted Uranus, but its moons would have remained on the same course as always, tilted at the angle Uranus had before it was struck.

Researchers have worked to explain the current state of Uranus by running different scenarios through the computer. Alessandro Morbidelli's team from the Observatoire de la Cote d'Azur in Nice, France ran a large number of simulations trying to figure out how Uranus and its moons could have ended up at 98° while moving in their current directions. He presented the best models at the 2011 EPSC-DPS Joint Meeting in Nantes, France, where he suggested that Uranus must have been bumped before the moons fully formed from the planet's protoplanetary disk. However, with only one big impact, the moons would have formed orbiting in a direction opposite to what we currently observe. The model with the best odds required Uranus to have experienced a couple of bumps in its history in order to get the planet and its moons close to their current tilts and orbits. Morbidelli explained:

> The standard planet formation theory assumes that Uranus, Neptune and the cores of Jupiter and Saturn formed by accreting only small objects in the protoplanetary disk. They should have suffered no giant collisions. The fact that Uranus was hit at least twice suggests that significant impacts were typical in the formation of giant planets. So, the standard theory has to be revised.[53]

---

52 Major, J. (2012, February 15). Venus Spinning Slower Than Thought - Scientists Stumped. *National Geographic News*. Retrieved January 9, 2018, from https://news.nationalgeographic.com/news/2012/02/120214-venus-planets-slower-spin-esa-space-science/

53 Europlanet. (2011, October 6). EPSC-DPS 2011/13: Series of Bumps Sent Uranus into Its Sideways Spin [Press release]. Retrieved January 9, 2018, from http://www.europlanet-eu.org/epsc-dps-201113-series-of-bumps-sent-uranus-into-its-sideways-spin

Ultimately, though, there's no real order or pattern for the rotation rates, axial tilts, or even the masses of the planets. The cosmogonists can try to model scenarios that explain *why* the tilts and rotation rates are what they are, but even if a model looks good, there's no way to know whether that scenario is actually what happened in history.

Cosmogonists have worked to explain some of the irregularities with the Nebular Theory, but these particular issues keep sticking out their noses. They have to create models for the simple reason that the solar system doesn't fit all that we'd expect from the Nebular Theory. There's plenty evidence of brutality out there in space during the history of the solar system. However, if the planets had been formed from the swirling dust of the solar nebulae, we would expect *some* kind of mathematical harmony.

THE FAINT YOUNG SUN PROBLEM

There are also timing issues. In 1972, Carl Sagan and George Mullen wrestled with what has come to be called "the faint young sun paradox."[54] If solar energy is the result of nuclear fusion as generally accepted, then the sun would have been much cooler four billion years ago. As hydrogen fuses into helium millennium after millennium, the sun's core would have grown increasingly dense, heating up and growing more luminous, which would make it about 40% brighter today (some say 25% brighter) than it was early in Earth's history.

This means that the young Earth *should* have been a much colder place than we now know, a veritable ball of ice 2.3 billion years ago. Yet, we know it couldn't have been that cold, because the rocks tell us there were oceans of liquid water in the young Earth. There have been temperature variations during the history of Earth, but they have been mild enough for life to persist since the Archean 3.8-2.5 billion years ago.

---

54 Sagan, C.; Mullen, G. (1972). Earth and Mars: Evolution of Atmospheres and Surface Temperatures. *Science*, 177 (4043): 52–56.

At the time of their paper, Sagan and Mullen suggested that higher ammonia (NH_3) and carbon dioxide (CO_2) levels in the Archean would have created a greenhouse effect to keep Earth's atmosphere warm despite the relative faintness of the sun. However, it's a simple fact that NH_3 naturally and rapidly converts to N_2 through photolysis, and it would have been a trick to keep NH_3 levels high enough for the necessary greenhouse warming affect. Archean-aged rocks from Greenland show that there was three times more CO_2 in the atmosphere of Earth at that time, but it still wouldn't have been sufficient to raise the mean temperature of Earth to liquefy seawater.[55] In a 2012 article, Georg Feulner reviews the various ideas on the matter and offers suggestions for further investigation.[56] He summarizes the issue saying:

> A wide range of possible solutions have been suggested and explored during the last four decades, with most studies focussing on higher concentrations of atmospheric greenhouse gases like carbon dioxide, methane or ammonia. All of these solutions present considerable difficulties, however, so the faint young Sun problem cannot be regarded as solved.

What bothers me is that nothing about any of this points to the planets having swirled into being out of the solar nebula. We do see that the planets are all swinging around the sun in the same direction and on the same plane, but there's a lot of messiness out there too. It's something worth investigating further.

---

55 Rosing, M.T. (2010). No Climate Paradox under the Faint Early Sun. *Nature*, 464: 744-747, doi:10.1038/nature08955.

56 Feulner G. (2012). The Faint Young Sun Problem. *Rev Geophys* 50:RG2006. Last accessed on January 14, 2018 at https://arxiv.org/pdf/1204.4449.pdf

Why The Book Finding Darwin's God Irritates Me

I don't normally go out of my way to criticize other authors. They wrote what they wrote. The readers can judge for themselves. I didn't just come across this book on my own, though; Dr. Derlidger suggested Kenneth Miller's book to me. Miller believes in God and he supports the evolution of all life on earth, and I think the Lidge figured his book would answer my questions and settle matters for me. It didn't. I did glean some interesting information, but the best thing the author did for me was to serve as a reminder to me to be cautious and humble.

1) Miller presumes to know the intentions and motivations of those he critiques.

Miller combats various Intelligent Design theorists in his book, which is fine. He's writing in support of evolutionary theory, with the idea that evolution created everything we see without any intervention from God in the process. That's the position he's taking, and I expect him to support it throughout his book. However, rather than just combatting the arguments of the I.D. theorists, Miller constantly insults them. It's super annoying. I would understand his attacking their general position or their specific arguments, but instead he attacks their character. He accuses them of being dishonest. Consider this example from page 108, in which Miller maligns popular I.D. theorist Phillip Johnson:

> Semantically, this is a brilliant strategy. You label any *observed* evolutionary mechanism as micromutational, say that yes, the work is interesting, but unfortunately the experiments at hand do not address the issue of macroevolution. By pretending that every example ever discovered of evolution in action is "just" microevolution, you can disqualify whole categories of important evidence against your case.

Okay, Miller just accused Johnson of being shady and dishonest. Tut tut, Kenneth Miller, Johnson might actually believe the things he said. I'm not bothered that Miller disagrees with Johnson's interpretation of the situation, and I'm not bothered that he thinks that Johnson is *wrong*. I'm bothered that Miller can't imagine that any thinking person could honestly have a different perspective than he does. I myself have seen a wide variety of cases that I too would describe as microevolution. I have seen no experiments that have convinced me that macroevolution has been experimentally demonstrated. I might have missed something, but my objection is intellectual, not philosophical.

What *should* Miller do here? He should go about the job of showing how the experiments in question really do apply to what would be required of macroevolution. He should do that. However, calling the arguments of his opponent "strategy" and accusing him of "pretending" is just a character assault.

On page 161, Miller says of biochemist Michael Behe:

> The great explanatory power of evolution comes, at least in part, from its ability to account for the sweeping changes in life that have occurred through natural history. Perhaps just a bit envious of this, Behe decided that the work of the [sic] God the mechanic had to be inserted into natural history too.

So, here Miller accuses Behe of being a stage-hog on God's behalf. That's so silly. Again, Miller doesn't give Behe the benefit of the doubt that intellectual satisfaction is Behe's primary concern.

I recognize that there have been a lot of people throughout the 19th and 20th centuries who have denied evolution for philosophical reasons. People have believed many completely ridiculous and inconvenient things for philosophical reasons. My gripe with Miller is that he assumes that philosophical issues are the *primary* reason that anybody would doubt microbes-to-man evolution. His whole book takes this approach. He's so convinced by the evidence for evolution of all life from amoebas, it seems he cannot imagine that other people have a serious logical struggle with it. Which leads to my second major problem with his book.

2) Miller briefly skims over issues that are full of controversy, makes gross generalizations, and treats his conclusions as self-evident.

As I read his book, I kept thinking, "Wait wait wait. That's not all there is to it! You treat with contempt those who take another viewpoint, but you are not appreciating the many problems with your own position. The case is not a little closed." Here is a clip from page 49 of *Finding Darwin's God*. I scrawled a variety of notes like this between the paragraphs.

Mutations are a continuing and inexhaustable source of variation, and they provide the raw material that is shaped by natural selection. Since mutations can duplicate, delete, invert, and rewrite any part of the genetic system in any organism, they can produce any change that evolution has documented. *You don't appreciate the extent of the problem.*

We watch bacterial mutations defeat antibiotics all the time. There's no question about it that bacteria swap genes and mutate, and they are in a little Red Queen race with antibiotics on a constant basis. However, mutating bacteria have nothing to say about what it takes to create wings and endocrine systems. No extrapolating to conclusions allowed in this area.

I've done enough computer programming to know how letter-for-letter computer codes have to be. Some variation in coding works, and some programs can break and the whole system can still function, but complicated codes do not magically write themselves through errors. DNA is a biological computer code, and this is a very complex, involved subject we'll save for another day.

To be fair, I recognize the difficulty of dealing with large issues in a small amount of space. Entire books have been written on subjects Miller deals with in a few sentences, and it's difficult to get through a lot of complicated material in a hurry. I know, because I'm trying to do it myself. The difference is that I'm not coming to hard conclusions on these issues. I recognize there's a whole lot of material to cover and I readily admit that I don't have the final answer on too much of anything.

At the same time, Miller repeatedly assigns to Intelligent Design the wildest arguments, which he then rejects. For instance, on page 95 when describing the trunks of various elephant-like species in the fossil record, he insists:

> Like it or not, intelligent design must face these data by arguing that each and every one of these species was designed from scratch…

That's just ridiculous. I don't know any design theorist who thinks each species was created from scratch and, in fact, that's the whole point of separating microevolution from macroevolution. Nobody has a problem with the evolution of different elephant-like species from a common ancestor. They just have a problem with the evolution of the elephant-like species from something that's not an elephant-like creature. Miller makes equally ridiculous claims over and over again, and I have scribbles in the margins of the book that repeatedly say, "Does anybody actually argue that?"

As we approach these difficult subjects, it's important we remember that the actual facts are always the important thing. Phillip Johnson's motives aren't really the issue. Kenneth R. Miller's motivations aren't the issue. Even the motives of biblical textual critics aren't the issue. Motivations don't change facts. It doesn't matter if a naked, hairy man emerges from a closet where he's been living on raw rats and tells you that the floorboards are rotten, or if a building inspector tells you the floorboards are rotten. The issue isn't who said it. The issue is, "Are the floorboards rotten?" We shouldn't waste time trying to explain why the naked guy complained about the floorboards – "He just wants us to feed him" – "He's crazy" – "He wants the floorboards to be rotten so he can force the rest of us into his rat-meat closet." It doesn't matter why he said it. Go investigate the stupid floorboards. We can certainly question the research of people with known motivations, and we should try to make sure their results can be duplicated, but if the floorboards are rotten, then they're rotten.

Collecting good data and carefully using those data to understand reality - those are appropriate goals. If we're going to focus on motives at all, we should be focused on our own - and keeping ourselves honest. If Kenneth R. Miller were standing in the room with me, I think he would agree with me on that.

Amy Joy, Sam, Savannah, and a Marvel hero at Snoqualmie Falls in 2010. The Amy Joy clan reportedly has a permanent dwelling in northern Idaho, but we can't promise you'll find them there.